DATE DUE			
Apr14 '81			

Cardano

THE GAMBLING SCHOLAR

Even if gambling were altogether an evil, still, on account of the very large number of people who play, it would seem to be a natural evil. For that very reason it ought to be discussed by a medical doctor like one of the incurable diseases.

CARDANO

Cardano

THE GAMBLING SCHOLAR

By Oystein Ore

WITH A TRANSLATION FROM THE LATIN
OF CARDANO'S *BOOK ON GAMES OF CHANCE*, BY
SYDNEY HENRY GOULD

PRINCETON, NEW JERSEY
PRINCETON UNIVERSITY PRESS
1953

London: Geoffrey Cumberlege, Oxford University Press

L.C. Card 52-13149

Printed in the United States of America by
Princeton University Press, Princeton, New Jersey

TO THE SCHOLARS OF
BRANFORD COLLEGE

Preface

THE RENAISSANCE bred many a man of genius and wrought many a fantastic life story, but even in such distinguished company does the life of Gerolamo Cardano, physician from Milan, readily catch the imagination. A brilliant start as a scholar, the rectorship of his university while he was a student, many years in attempting to build a professional career, all brought him only to the humiliating state where, with wife and child, he had to seek shelter in the poorhouse. But from here he began a one-man frontal attack upon the practices of the medical profession in his day with such success that some years later he ranked with his friend Vesalius in the forefront of the physicians of the world, and with flattering offers the crowned heads of Europe vied for his services.

Cardano's entertaining books on science and curiosities were among the best read and most pirated works in the sixteenth century and, together with his books on consolation and comfort to the suffering, they were spread all over Europe. As a mathematician Cardano was probably the leader in his century; his work on the "Great Art" has been characterized as the first that goes decisively beyond the attainments of the giants of classical Greek mathematics.

Yet all this was not sufficient to insure his happiness, not even to keep him from misery and from jail. One son was executed as a murderer; the other was a habitual criminal who brought his father nothing but sorrow. In his old age Cardano was incarcerated as a heretic and stricken from the university rolls, yet he ended his days peacefully in Rome as a pensioner of the pope.

This is primarily the story of Cardano's life, his beliefs —and his superstitions, which earned for him a doubtful place of distinction next to Paracelsus and Nostradamus among the exponents of occult lore. It is also an account of Renaissance scholarship and university life with its jealousies, intrigues, and violent public disputes; Cardano was the center of some of the most celebrated scientific controversies of the sixteenth century.

There is one of Cardano's fervent activities for which he has been unanimously reproached by his biographers—his gambling. By his own admission he gambled continually. But since he always kept an observant eye on his own actions as a human being, and since his speculative mind utilized them all, even his vices, to produce information which he could systematize in his writings, it is no wonder that he composed a learned book on games and ways to win in gambling. This is still an entertaining document, and even at present it contains good advice for gamblers.

Most important for the history of science is the fact that *Liber de Ludo Aleae*, "The Book on Games of Chance," contains the first study of the principles of probability. But the praise which Cardano has received for this great achievement is much more scant than he deserves. The reason for this reticence is fairly evident, and certain historians of mathematics have not hesitated to say in plain words: some of the calculations of chance in the *Ludo Aleae* have appeared unintelligible to them. Thus it also becomes one of the tasks of this book to elucidate Cardano's gambling studies. As a result I have gained the conviction that this pioneer work on probability is so extensive and in certain questions so successful that it would seem much more just to date the beginnings of probability theory from Cardano's treatise rather than the customary reckoning from Pascal's discussions with his gambling friend de Méré and the ensuing correspondence with Fermat, all of which took place at least a century after Cardano began composing his *De Ludo Aleae.*

My thanks go first to Professor S. H. Gould of Purdue University for his translation from the Latin of *Liber de*

Ludo Aleae, given at the end of this book. It is correct to say that in some measure the translation has been a co-operative effort, and my appreciation should also be expressed to the eminent classical scholar G. L. Hendrickson of Yale University; as my own understanding of some of the more technical parts increased I have permitted myself to make a few changes in the text and to add some foot-notes to elucidate certain technical points. But the larger share of the credit goes to Professor Gould whose combined skill as a mathematician and a classical scholar made him singularly fitted for such a task. His renditions have greatly facilitated the unraveling of Cardano's thought, and I am happy to have him take official responsibility for the translation by affixing his name to it.

For certain other Latin translations I am also indebted to Professor Hendrickson and to Professor Gould. For assistance with certain early Italian documents I must express my sincere gratitude to Dr. Salvatore Bottino of Rome.

It is also a pleasant duty to acknowledge that the book has been greatly improved through the expert advice and assistance which I have received from the editorial staff of the Princeton University Press.

OYSTEIN ORE

New Haven, Connecticut
September 1952

Contents

Preface vii

1. The Stormy Life of Cardano 3

2. Cardano's Enigmatic Character 25

3. The Battles of the Scholars 53

4. Cardano, the Gambler 108

5. The Science of Gambling 143

Bibliography 178

LIBER DE LUDO ALEAE

The Book on Games of Chance
by Gerolamo Cardano, translated by
Sydney Henry Gould 181

Index 243

Illustrations

1. Cardano's horoscope 4
2. An early woodcut of Milan 6
3. University buildings in Padua 8
4. Cardano's suggestion for raising a sunken vessel 16
5. Cardano's improvement of the draft in a chimney 18
6. Cardano's proposal for an improved lamp 20
7. A cipher lock suggested by Cardano 26
8. Cabalistic symbolism 29
9. Cardano's studies on clockworks 32
10. Amulet belonging to Cardano 35
11. An illustration of divination from the position of warts 36
12. Furnace and chemistry vessels for distillation 38
13. Cardano's conception of the blood circulation 45
14. Cardano's proposal for a condensed system of writing numbers 49
15. Multiple Archimedes screw for irrigation purposes 51
16. The Terrible Scaliger 56
17. Niccolò Tartaglia 64
18. Study of fall motion 70
19. Tartaglia's instrument for determining distances 73

20. Tartaglia's instrument for measuring elevation 76
21. The various intellectual levels of games 110
22. Cardano's suspension for a compass 121
23. A geomancy chart 139
24. A chiromancy chart 141
25. Italian cards from Cardano's time 173
26. The wheel of fortune 180
27. Tessera 193
28. Astragals 193
29. A backgammon board 230

Plates

The plates may be found in the section following page 98.

1. Painting of Lord Burleigh playing primero, ascribed to Zuccaro
2. Gerolamo Cardano at the age of sixty-eight
3. Playing cards printed in Milan about the time of Cardano
4. A reproduction from "The Cardsharps" by Caravaggio

Cardano
THE GAMBLING SCHOLAR

The Stormy Life of Cardano

GEROLAMO CARDANO or Jerome Cardan was born in the year 1501, and thus most appropriately he barely escapes being recorded in the Middle Ages. He was probably of illegitimate birth although Cardano hotly denies this and ascribes the "false rumors" to circumstances which compelled his parents to live apart for many years. However, he does admit in his autobiography that he had heard that he was born in spite of several attempted abortions. Whatever the truth may be, it was to cause him many disagreeable experiences and much professional trouble during his career in Milan. There has also been some disagreement as to the exact date of his birth; this may in part be due to errors by his biographers and in part due to Cardano's own lapses of memory, especially by misstatements in his various testaments, but there seems to be no reason to doubt the date used in his horoscopes which he cast personally. They are based on the exact time of his birth: September 24 in the year 1501 at six hours and forty minutes from the meridian.

Cardano was a man of universal interests, and much of his ability must have been inherited from his father, Fazio Cardano. Fazio or Bonifacius was a lawyer in Milan, but also deeply steeped in the medical sciences, mathematics, and in all kinds of occult lore. He never made much money and his profession as a jurisconsult never seems to have occupied him particularly, but he had, nevertheless, a high reputation as a scholar in his native town; even Leonardo da Vinci notes several times that he consulted Messer Fazio on geometric questions. His only published work was an edition with commentary of *De Perspectivis Communis* by John Peckham (1240-1292), the archbishop of Canterbury, which was printed in 1480.

At one time Fazio Cardano gave lectures on geometry at his alma mater, the University of Pavia. A few years after

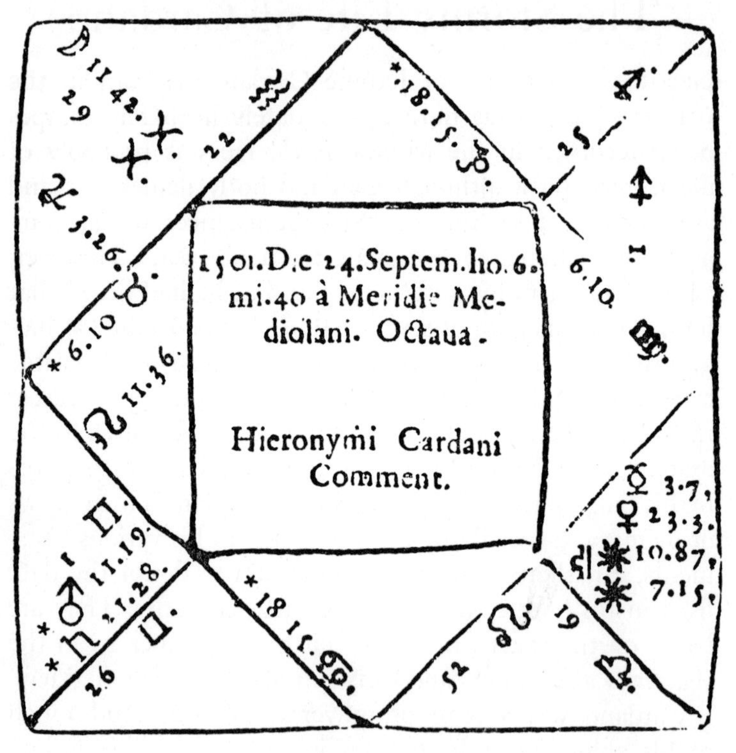

1. Cardano's horoscope. From *Liber De Exemplis Centum Geniturarum.*

the birth of young Gerolamo the scholar Tommasso Piatti in his will created a foundation in Milan for the instruction of poor youths and here Fazio was appointed as a public lecturer in geometry. It was economically a very modest position, but it seems to have suited Fazio Cardano's temperament perfectly.

He met Gerolamo's mother, Chiara Michena, quite late in life, and she was a good deal younger. Evidently she came from rather lowly circumstances and was not "socially acceptable" in Milan, so Fazio preferred to support her separately; however, gradually he became so accustomed to the situation that he moved into the same house and they were married a short time before his death. When Fazio first made Chiara Michena's acquaintance she was a widow with three children from a previous marriage. The plague reached Milan when she expected her new child and she was compelled to flee. Gerolamo was born at the home of some wealthy friends in Pavia, but meanwhile tragedy struck and all her other children perished in the epidemic. The son was always deeply devoted to his mother; he described her vividly as "small of stature, fat, pious, and of quick temper."

Cardano's life is known in considerable detail. His voluminous writings are interspersed with personal anecdotes, sometimes of the most revealing kind. His autobiography, *De Propria Vita,* was written when he was a very old man. Although it shows certain signs of his beginning senility, it is a forceful story and has been translated into many languages. It is filled with frank but naturally somewhat flavored information about his experiences and views. In connection with his horoscope he passes the judgment upon himself that among his good qualities "there remains only a certain keenness of mind and a soul easily influenced by passion and full of foolhardy and impossible schemes. Since I lacked physical strength, had few friends, little luck, many enemies which I to a great extent did not even know by name or sight, was without human understanding and had a bad memory, I could only claim, in one word, a certain advantage in the matter of foresight. Therefore, I do not understand why my condition, which was lowly from the point of view of family and ancestors, has been deemed so glorious and worthy of envy."

He tells about his physical characteristics at great length:

he was of medium height, with such small feet that he had difficulty in getting well-fit shoes, his chest was narrow, his arms thin, the neck long, the chin was cleft, heavy lower lip, a wart over one eye, and so on. He had light hair in his youth and wore it short, like his beard, which he parted into two points. His voice was rude and he spoke so

2. An early woodcut of Milan. From *Liber Chronicarum* (1493).

loudly that it was irritating even to his friends. He delights equally in describing all the diseases which he has suffered, fluxes, ruptures, kidney trouble, palpitation of the heart, all with unsavory details down to an infection of a nipple. At the time of writing he had only fourteen teeth in good condition and a weak one, which he hoped would continue to give good service. He laments in numerous places that he was sexually impotent from the age of twenty-one until shortly before his marriage at thirty-one.

As the boy Cardano grew up he was helpful to his father, but became more of a servant than he liked. He was anxious to get an education beyond the instruction which he received at home, but Fazio objected to sending him away. It came to a violent argument in the Cardano household, with Chiara supporting her son. She pleaded and raged until she finally fainted and hurt her head, and in the face of this commotion Fazio had to give in. So, at the age of nineteen, Gerolamo was permitted to go to his father's old university in Pavia to study medicine.

Only a year afterward the institution had to close when war broke out between Emperor Charles V of Spain and King Francis I of France. Cardano then transferred to the University of Padua, which was under the protection of Venice, and thus a relatively peaceful place.

In Padua young Gerolamo began to assert himself and to show some of his remarkable abilities. He was a brilliant student and was even deemed worthy of participating in the public disputes, the scholarly duels of the day. According to his own reports, which are never overly modest, he acquitted himself well and even defeated some of the members of the faculty. He was a storm center among the students, and his vanity led him to accept the rectorship of the university, an honor which he later sincerely regretted. This was a yearly appointment, and Cardano's majority in the balloting was a single vote. At one time the rectorship in Italian universities, usually held by a student, had been an important position, but by this time it had become an almost empty distinction which mostly could be filled only with the sons of high nobles or rich wastrels who could afford the heavy expenses for student entertainment which the office required.

Cardano had no great resources, but at about this time his father died and he used his small patrimony to cover the expenses of his office. According to his own description he led a frivolous student life and gambling was not only his favorite pastime but also his main source of income. At this time he began gathering his first notes on the subject of chance and probability, the preliminary studies for his book on gambling.

When Cardano was about twenty-five years of age his university studies were completed and he disputed for his doc-

3. University buildings in Padua. From an old print.

torate. The opinions were obviously greatly divided; some of the opposition may have been caused by personal animosity (all during his life Cardano had a remarkable facility for creating both friends and foes). The first ballot denied him the degree of Doctor of Medicine with 47 votes against 9, a second ballot still refused him, but on the third and deciding ballot the original score was reversed, 47 in favor and 9 opposed.

He was now ready to begin his lifework and immediately applied for admission to the College of Physicians in Milan so that he might be permitted to practice in his home town where his mother still lived. However, one of the reporters on his candidacy brought out the fact that he was of illegitimate birth and, since this was contrary to the statutes, his membership was refused. Now bastardy was not usually taken too seriously and it was in the power of the college to disregard this circumstance, had they been so inclined, particularly since the facts were in dispute. From the subsequent development of the case it appears that Cardano must have had some active antagonists within the college and the refusal was in reality not based so much upon his social standing or his medical qualifications as upon his reputation for aggressiveness and for outspoken and critical opinions.

After this setback Cardano, upon the advice of friends at the university, decided to settle as a country doctor in the little village of Sacco, a few miles outside of Padua. He does not appear to have had much of a practice and it was no place to prosper, but later in his life he always looked back upon these years in Sacco as the happiest in his life. On this subject he philosophizes in *De Propria Vita*:

"Although even the notion of happiness is far from our nature, nevertheless, it does happen that we may attain a part of it, as far as happiness may be realized. Therefore, I have also had my share in it, indeed, it is even clear that I have been favored among mortals in this respect.

"All that has happened to me has come with such rule and precision that, if it had appeared a little earlier or a little later, everything would have been thrown completely into disorder.

"Secondly, let me single out a special period in my life for comparison with the rest: this was the time I lived in Sacco. Among the giants there is necessarily a smallest and among the pygmies necessarily one who is the greatest, without the giant being small or the pygmy great. So, even if I experienced a certain happiness in Sacco, it does not follow that I have ever been truly happy. But then I gambled, played musical instruments, took walks, and was of good cheer and studied only rarely. I had no pains, no fears; I was treated with esteem and respect and I associated with the nobles of Venice. In short, it was the springtime of my life. I have never known a more agreeable life than these five and a half years, from September 1526 to February 1532. I knew the mayor, and the city hall was my kingdom and rostrum. That time has passed, but the memory gives me an impression of pleasure and I am carried back to it in my dreams."

In Sacco he married Lucia Bandarini, the daughter of an innkeeper and captain of the local Venetian militia, and this marriage was as happy as Cardano's nature could make it. However, it became evident that he could not support a family in Sacco. His repeated applications to the College of Physicians in Milan were all turned down, and in 1532 he decided to move to the little town of Gallarate near Milan, the home of some of his ancestors. He had often visited Gallarate with his father in the summer, and he still had some relatives there. But things went from bad to worse, and after his first child was born—a boy, Giambatista—he moved again, this time back to Milan where he actually had to seek shelter in the poorhouse with his family.

At this low point in his career Cardano's luck changed and the rise toward fame began. Among the nobles in Milan he found friends who were interested in scientific questions. Many of them must have known his father and through their influence he was appointed to his father's old position as public lecturer on the Piatti foundation. He made a strong effort to attract large audiences by giving interesting and entertaining lectures. Not only did he succeed well but he also laid the groundwork for his later books on popular science.

As a lecturer in mathematics Cardano had to devote considerable time to this topic. In 1539 he published his first two mathematical books, one a computer for the layman (*Libellus Qui Dicitur Computus Minor*) and the second a much more ambitious textbook, *The Practice of Arithmetic and Simple Mensuration* (*Practica Arithmetica et Mensurandi Singularis*). It did not have the depth of some of his later mathematical works, but it was one of the best and most influential books of its kind, and some sections are quite original.

In the way of advertisement it was prefaced with a verse by the poet Annibale della Croce:

Many are the uses of numbers and their various parts
But here in a small, learned and easily digested book
Cardano explains them to you with diligent care
Read it and you will say
I owe as much to it as to the thousand volumes.

The honorarium for the book was ten gold crowns to the needy author. The frontispiece gave his portrait surrounded by the bitter legend, "No man is a prophet in his own country." But Cardano expressed the hope that the work would recommend him to scholars in other countries, and appended to it a list of all the books he had written but which were still unpublished. His expectations were fulfilled not long after when he received an offer from the German printer Johannes Petreius in Nürnberg to publish whatever manuscripts he might have on hand, a very liberal offer indeed. "This was the beginning of my fame; whatever glory I may have achieved, this was the origin."

During these years Cardano supplemented his meager income as a lecturer by treating occasional patients recommended by his friends; this may not have been a legal practice since the College of Physicians was adamant in its refusal of his repeated requests for admission. But he effected several outstanding cures and in some desperate cases he even seems to have been called in as a consultant by his Milanese colleagues. Thus he gradually acquired more friends and also some reputation as a physician, although his ability was usually deprecated by jealous rivals.

Cardano then changed his tactics. He decided he had nothing to lose and began a violent offensive against the college. In 1536, through the aid of an intimate university friend, Ottaviano Scotto, who had become a printer in Venice, he succeeded in getting published his first book, *On the Bad Practices of Medicine in Common Use* (*De Malo Recentiorum Medicorum Medendi Usu Libellus*). It was dedicated to his very good friend Filippo Archinto, who later had a distinguished career in the service of the church and ended his days as Archbishop in Milan. In the book Cardano on the whole shows good medical sense and lists various common procedures which he considers erroneous and harmful. This may have been irritating enough for his exclusive colleagues in Milan, but what enraged them most was his vicious thrusts against their pompous habits and deportment: "The things which give most reputation to a physician nowadays are his manners, servants, carriage, clothes, smartness, and caginess, all displayed in a sort of artificial and insipid way; learning and experience seem to count for nothing."

According to Cardano the book was written in a fortnight and, since no proofs could be obtained from Venice, it naturally contained an abundance of errors, a fact which Cardano later readily admitted. The practitioners in Milan made the most of these deficiencies and heaped scorn upon the author of such an inept work. But they could not prevent public interest from becoming aroused by this barrage of criticism and ridicule of the medical profession, and in the face of such aggressive attacks the position of the college became quite embarrassing. They first attempted to satisfy Cardano with a half concession, permitting him to practice only in consultation with physicians in full standing with the board, certainly a most humiliating and unsatisfactory condition for an experienced doctor. Early in 1539 Cardano again appeared before the board, this time with influential and prominent sponsors, and the college finally found it wise to relent. They agreed to modify the clause in their constitution requiring legitimate birth, to allow persons born out of wedlock to be admitted to membership if they had later been legitimized by the marriage of their parents. This obviously covered Cardano's case and he was duly elected a member.

The consequences of this action were catastrophic in a way that some of his opponents in the college had probably foreseen. Within a few years Cardano was the rector of the guild and without question the most prominent physician in Milan. Before he was fifty years old Cardano was second only to Vesalius among European physicians and was overwhelmed with flattering and magnificent offers for his services. The pope and Europe's royal and imperial heads with their princely families were convinced that no physician could better safeguard their health than Cardano. "So it came that when I ought to have been dead I began to live," he wrote.

Cardano accepted few of these offers; the life as a court physician with intrigues and restrictions and fits of royal temper did not appeal to him. Only one call took him far from his beloved Milan; this was a mission in response to a very generous offer from John Hamilton, the Archbishop of Scotland who, as a brother of the regent James Hamilton, Earl of Arran, exerted great political influence in the troubled years of the childhood of Mary, Queen of Scots. The archbishop suffered from suffocating attacks of asthma which had grown steadily worse, and his physician, the

Frenchman Cassanate, had exhausted his own resources and advised him to turn to Cardano for possible relief.

Cardano was not anxious to go, but the financial advantages were remarkable, and so early in 1552 he set out from Milan with a small retinue. He traveled through Lyons, Paris, Boulogne to Calais, and from there by ship to London; on the return trip he selected the route through Antwerp, Cologne, Strasbourg, and Basel. Cardano was at this time at the height of his fame, as a practicing physician he was unequaled, and his books were read everywhere by laymen and scientists alike. Wherever he went his visits were the occasion for festive gatherings of prominent doctors and scientists; in France he was given a large military escort, and in England the king requested his presence.

The consultation in Edinburgh took considerable time, so long that some of his Italian servants made a nuisance of themselves in town, but the results of his treatments were evidently most satisfactory. When after a few months he desired to return to Milan, Archbishop Hamilton was very reluctant to see him go, but gave him 1,800 gold crowns as a fee and a heavy gold chain as a personal gift. During his stay in Scotland Cardano had also been besieged by noble patients and the rewards for these consultations strongly belied the reputation which this part of the world has long enjoyed.

Even in his adolescent years Cardano had begun to write compositions and gather notes on a variety of topics. After his first books had appeared, his efforts were intensified and one great work after the other came from the press. He wrote on mathematics, astronomy and physics, on moral questions, on dialectics, on death, on the immortality of the soul, the mysteries of eternity, in praise of Nero, on music, on games of chance, on chess, on gems, on dreams, on wisdom, on the lives of Christ and the Blessed Virgin, and a host of other topics too numerous to mention. More than half of his books were on medical questions: general treatises on medical practices and the art of healing, descriptions of some of his cures, as well as special studies on potions, poisons, air and water, proper nourishment, prevention of disease, living conditions, the plague, urine, teeth, the works of Galen and Hippocrates, and much else.

Cardano's published works were numerous, yet a much greater amount of manuscript material remained unpublished after his death. In his autobiography he presents a list many pages long containing only the titles of his works, and he even published a special little personal bibliography giving a survey of his production. From time to time he burned large masses of writings which he found unsatisfactory.

To the lay public in Europe Cardano became well known through his popular scientific and philosophical books, some of them appearing in many editions and translations. His anecdotal way of presenting his thoughts and his bizarre illustrations appealed greatly to a public unaccustomed to much entertainment from the authors of the serious and pedantic medieval texts. Foremost in this new trend in writing stands *De Subtilitate Rerum*, a collection of discussions on science and natural philosophy enlivened with a varied mixture of illustrations and interspersed with superstitions and strange tales. During the second half of the sixteenth century it was one of the best sellers in popular literature, and the inefficiency of the copyright restrictions made it an easy prey for printers outside of Italy. His book on *The Variety of Things* (*De Rerum Varietate*) was of a similar nature but somewhat less successful.

His books on ethics and philosophy in general, for instance the books on *Wisdom* and *Consolation*, also had wide circulation. The latter, *Comforte* as it was called in the first English translation of 1573 by Beddingfield, was a book of comfort and resignation for those besieged by sorrows. The introductory epistle expresses the purpose quaintly:

4. Cardano's suggestion for raising a sunken vessel. The wreck is lifted slightly by jettisoning the stones in the small boats so that the vessel gradually can be moved to shallow water. From *De Subtilitate*.

Your troubled mindes with torments lost
That sighs and sobs consumes:
Come reade this book that freely bringes
A box of balm full sweete,
An oyl to noynt the brused partes
Of every heavye spirete.

The lame whose lacke of legges
Is death unto a loftye mynde
Will kisse his crotche and creepe on knees
Cardanus woorkes to fynde.

Cardano's wife Lucia died in 1546 when she was only thirty-one years old, leaving him with three children. The oldest, Giambatista, was then twelve years of age; the daughter Chiara, named for her grandmother, was ten; and the youngest, Aldo, was a baby of three. Cardano wrote a book on the education of children, but with his patients, his scientific studies, and his writing it does not seem likely that he had much time to devote to the bringing up of his own. Besides, in most things he inclined more toward theory than practice.

Giambatista was his father's favorite, and Cardano helped him in every way to follow in his own footsteps. The boy completed his medical studies in Pavia and did quite well, but for some unknown reason he had, like his father, some difficulty before he was admitted to practice in Milan. Cardano believed that his son had great gifts, but the father was hardly an impartial judge. Possibly encouraged by him, Giambatista did write a few minor essays on medical themes, which the father carefully preserved.

The family prospered as the boys grew up. Cardano was professor of medicine in nearby Pavia for many years. This, in addition to his practice, produced a good income, so that he was looking forward to a more leisurely old age.

Then suddenly tragedy struck and his existence turned into misery. As usual he had a premonition before the important event. All seemed to go well when he retired in the evening of December 20, 1557. But during the night the bed and the whole house began to tremble so that it was noticed even by the servants. In the morning a messenger

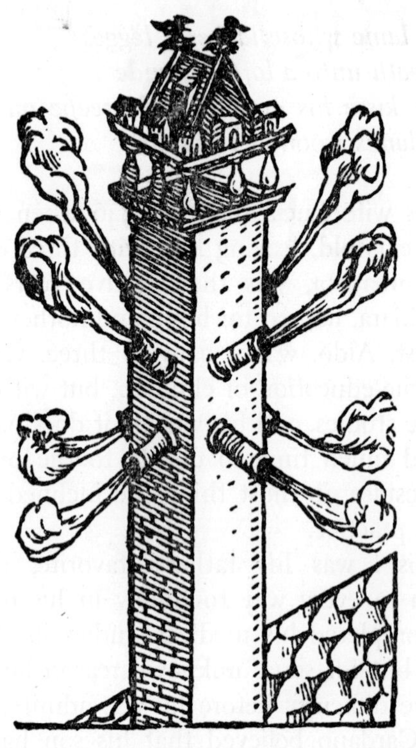

5. Cardano's improvement of the draft in a chimney. From *De Subtilitate.*

arrived from Milan announcing that Giambatista had suddenly married the girl he loved, Brandonia Seroni. This was truly the beginning of all his misfortunes, as Cardano comments.

Brandonia was known as a highly disreputable girl. Cardano preferred not to have the young couple living in his house, but he continued to support the son financially. Young Giambatista moved in with his wife's relatives, but the marriage was anything but harmonious. His wife's relatives exploited him mercilessly while she after a short time was shamelessly unfaithful to him. Three children were born in rapid succession, and the last, a boy, was named Fazio for Giambatista's grandfather. After his birth the quarrels broke out again more violently than ever, and Brandonia chided her husband openly for not being the father of any of her children.

This brought Giambatista's wrath to overflow. He ordered a servant to bake a cake, mixed the flour with arsenic, and poisoned his wife and at the same time very nearly several of her relatives as well. He was arrested immediately with the servant and a few days afterward made a full confession. Cardano supported his son in every possible way; he hired excellent lawyers, testified in court on his behalf, wrote petitions, and appealed for clemency through all his friends and influential patients. But it was all to no avail: Giambatista was sentenced to death and executed shortly after on April 10, 1560, not quite twenty-six years old. On the way to the execution he was tortured and his left hand was struck off.

Cardano never recovered from the loss of his son. He reproached himself, wrote elegies to him, brooded, and relived the tragic events incessantly. In Milan and Pavia everything reminded the old man of his sorrows. His position as the father of a murderer was painful, and he retired to his own house where for a while he even tried to give his lectures. Finally he could suffer it no longer and resigned his professorship. Through the intervention of some of his old friends he received a call to the University of Bologna as professor of medicine.

In the fall of 1562 Cardano moved to his new post. His daughter Chiara had married, but his nineteen-year-old son Aldo accompanied him, although this certainly gave his father no pleasure. He was an out and out scoundrel who kept bad company, wasted his father's money, and caused endless trouble by his escapades. He had already begun a criminal career and had seen the inside of the jails in several Italian cities. Cardano's great consolation was his grandson

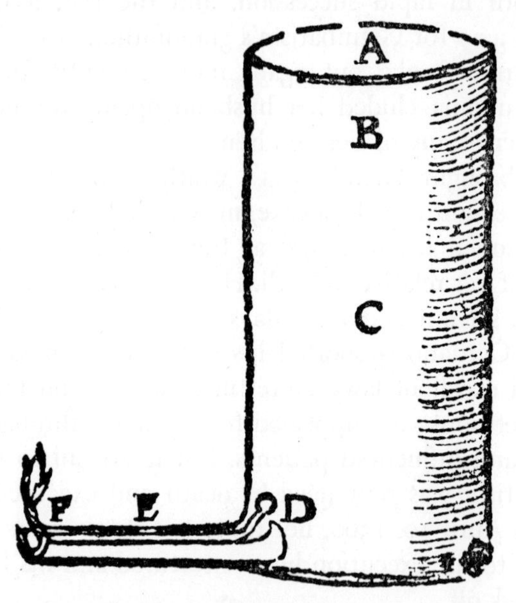

6. Cardano's proposal for an improved lamp. The oil is maintained in the container by vacuum. From *De Subtilitate.*

Fazio, whom he adopted and later took with him everywhere.

In Bologna Cardano had several good friends on the faculty, the new surroundings were beneficial to him, and he regained his equilibrium. He occupied himself with writings and medical lectures and was considered one of the most distinguished scholars at the university. It flattered him greatly when the City of Bologna bestowed honorary citizenship upon him to replace what he had lost in Milan.

As usual Cardano had a few disagreements with some of his colleagues in Bologna, but the only real source of trouble was his son Aldo's behavior. Aldo no longer lived in his father's house, but his various demands were frequent and expensive. At one time he had to be salvaged from Rome when he had gambled away 300 scudi of his father's money as well as all his own clothes and equipment. The climax was reached in 1569 when Aldo and one of Cardano's assistants burglarized the house, broke open an iron strong box, and escaped with a large sum of money, jewelry, and precious stones, some of them amulets which Cardano particularly valued.

Cardano in desperation reported the theft to the authorities, who soon apprehended the scoundrels; some of the jewelry was recovered. The assistant was sentenced to the galleys and Aldo, upon the request of his father, was banished from Bologna and its surrounding territories. Nevertheless, after a time it seems that Cardano and Aldo came to some sort of an understanding and Aldo wrote a submissive letter of confession in which he admitted, among other things, that he had been jailed no less than eight times for various wrongdoings.

Fate had reserved a final staggering blow for Cardano's declining years. On October 6, 1570, he was arrested without warning and put in jail, accused of being a heretic. The immediate cause for this action has never become quite clear. Some writers have conjectured that the enraged Aldo may have denounced his father, but the documents give no support for such a charge and it seems unlikely that a youth of his standing would have gained much credence. It was rather the Counter-Reformation, which at this time was gaining momentum. The severely orthodox Pope Pius V and some of his cardinals had already used the inquisition for drastic action against prominent men whose wholehearted support of the Catholic Church was in doubt, and the works of all authors were examined with minute care.

In the profuse writings of Cardano it was not difficult to find statements which could be construed as being impious: it was manifest that he had conceived the grotesque idea of casting the horoscope of Jesus Christ; he had written a book in praise of Emperor Nero, the tormentor of the martyrs, to demonstrate that even the worst natures can have their laudable sides; in *Subtility* he had inserted a dialogue in which the pros and cons of Christianity were discussed in comparison with other religions, but without statements which could be considered offensive. In the subsequent work on *The Variety of Things* a Swiss printer had taken advantage of Cardano and inserted a derogatory statement about the Dominican Order, but this fraud had been exposed immediately and the passages were expurgated from the subsequent edition.

Cardano was now a man close to the biblical age of three score and ten. He had never shown any actively hostile attitude toward the church and was submissive before the tribunal, so the fathers of the inquisition were relatively lenient. He had the sympathy of public opinion in Bologna, and several students testified in his favor. He was kept in jail for a few months, apparently without torture, and his pupil and faithful friend, Rodolfo Silvestri, was permitted to attend to his needs. Later he was allowed to live in his own house under surveillance.

Cardano was always voluble in explaining his actions, but his *Autobiography* does not contain a single word about the nature of the proceedings under the inquisition. Evidently he was sworn to secrecy before his release. The only work mentioned as objectionable in the records was *De Rerum Varietate,* and the corrected edition had then already been in print for more than a dozen years. It is difficult to escape the impression that Cardano's case was selected rather to serve as a statutory warning than because of any urgency to combat his heretical views.

The sentence was not extreme; indeed, the inquisitor general may have thought it merciful, but it deprived Cardano of all the things which still seemed worth while to him in life. He was permitted to abjure privately, rather than in the customary and most humiliating ceremony in which the victim stands barefoot before the congregation, clad only in the shirt of the penitents and with a lighted candle in his hand, deploring his beliefs and singing the hymns of conversion. But he was stricken from the university rolls and denied the right to lecture publicly, and above all, he was forbidden to have any more of his books printed.

Rodolfo Silvestri, his loyal pupil, took a hand in the old man's life from this point. They journeyed to Rome together where Silvestri wanted to practice, and to Cardano it did not matter too much, except that he had a relative and former student, Gaspare Cardano, who was already well established in the city. He also had a faint hope of obtaining a commutation of his sentence through the influence of some of his friends among the cardinals.

The reception in Rome was surprisingly favorable. The College of Physicians invited him to membership and occasionally he took part in a consultation or post-mortem. His friend Silvestri prospered and made a name for himself. Cardano still had some personal means and he relates, strangely enough, that in addition he had been granted a pension by the pope. He could not cease writing books; his last manuscript was *De Propria Vita* in which he accounts for his life, his sorrows and joys, successes and failures, and the qualities and deficiencies of his character. In the résumé of his books he counts 131 printed works, and after he had burned 170 manuscripts which he considered useless there still remained 111 books in manuscript.

Gerolamo Cardano died peacefully on September 20, 1576, close to seventy-five years old. He wished to be buried in Milan in the Church of the Augustins in San Marco. Cardano willed almost his entire estate to young Fazio, his grandson, except for a small pension which was awarded the misguided Aldo on certain specified conditions. The books and the manuscripts were left in the care of Silvestri. Some were scattered and lost later, but a number of the posthumous manuscripts are included in the magnificent edition of Cardano's works, ten huge volumes altogether, which appeared in Lyons in 1663.

Cardano's Enigmatic Character

CARDANO's character was an enigma to many of his contemporaries and it must be admitted that it has remained so to most of his biographers through the centuries which have passed. He is a man who has been praised and vilified; by some he has been called a genius, by others a poseur, some have presented him as a benefactor to mankind, others frankly believed him to be an evil spirit, indeed, a monster. One should expect that the analysis of his works would eventually bring a satisfactory clarification, but unfortunately his books can give some support to almost any view. The possibilities for a just evaluation on this basis are complicated still further not only by direct contradictions but also by many instances where it is impossible to escape the feeling that he is insincere. What, for instance, should one make of a man who is capable in one breath of characterizing himself as follows:

"Nature has made me capable in all manual work, it has given me the spirit of a philosopher and ability in the sciences, taste and good manners, voluptuousness, gaiety, it has made me pious, faithful, fond of wisdom, meditative, inventive, courageous, fond of learning and teaching, eager to equal the best, to discover new things and make independent progress, of modest character, a student of medicine, interested in curiosities and discoveries, cunning, crafty, sarcastic, an initiate in the mysterious lore, industrious, diligent, ingenious, living only from day to day, impertinent, contemptuous of religion, grudging, envious, sad, treacherous, magician and sorceror, miserable, hateful, lascivious, solitary, disagreeable, rude, divinator, envious, lascivious, obscene, lying, obsequious, fond of the prattle of old men, changeable, irresolute, indecent, fond of women, quarrelsome, and because of the conflicts between my nature and soul I am not understood even by those with whom I associate most frequently."

Part of this mysteriousness may have been intentional. Other early physicians are known to have affected a strangeness of manner, supposedly a desirable trait in the struggle to maintain their reputation. The art of healing was still but a small step removed from magic, and their public was not only highly impressionable but expected to be impressed.

7. A cipher lock suggested by Cardano. The cogs on the alphabet wheels would only permit opening when forming the code word Serpens. From *De Subtilitate*.

Cardano speaks about his secretiveness in many places, for instance in a little allegorical tale in the *Autobiography*. The family escutcheon of the Cardanos carried a small tower, but, as he tells with a touch of pride, it resembled so closely the arms of the distinguished Castiglione family that it was deemed advisable to change it. The emperor had granted permission to add an eagle with spreading wings. "However, just on the day on which I was arrested, I had adopted for my own seal a swallow singing under a gable because the other attributes were very difficult to reproduce. I chose the swallow because in many ways it reminds me of my own character. It is incapable of causing harm, it does not shun the company of the poor, and although it lives constantly near humans it never becomes intimate with them. It changes its abode often, comes and goes; it is not lonesome nor in a crowd, but loves its family. It chirps to entertain its hosts and cannot suffer living in a cage. It is the only animal which can recover its sight after having lost it and in its small body it carries some precious calculi. It loves especially the warm air and a mild climate. It builds its nest with great skill and in this respect it is not surpassed by any other bird, except the halcyon. It is white underneath and black for the rest. It returns to its old nest as if it had both memory and gratefulness. No birds, not even the birds of prey, pursue it, because none of them can overtake it or even equal it in flight."

Cardano often expresses regret over the small number of true friends he has attracted, but he cannot feign feelings which he does not possess. Toward the end of *De Propria Vita* he writes:

"I was useless in conversation and entertainment and this was also one of the reasons why I avoided large banquets. However, I never repulsed good and honest people, particularly not those who were miserable or reasonable persons or those toward whom I had obligations.

"But you may argue: man is a sociable animal and what is the purpose in renouncing your friends and every influence in the world? What, however, will you be able to do? You may boast of having influential friends. This is a vain boast and what does it serve? Since there are people who know well how to please these great persons, with table talk, jokes, and games, why do you think that they will leave these flatterers to love you? What is the use of your science if it is of no interest to them? 'Your knowledge is nothing if no one knows that you know.' Finally, not having the requisite natural gifts, you will suffer many disappointments.

"I know all the objections which can be made, but I am also aware of the fact that many things which appear painful and absurd at first may change and conversely, many agreeable and useful things may later take on a painful aspect. And my own way of behaving is mostly sufficient to preserve for me those friends which I have mentioned who have received me into their friendship. Actually, they suffice for me and they are more reliable and beneficial than a crowd of others."

During his lifetime Cardano was criticized on many scores. His personal conduct was certainly not always above reproach. His pushing and arrogant ways made him disliked by some, others objected to his tendency to self-glorification and to his criticisms, while to some his unsystematic and self-centered way of writing, combined with an awkward Latin style, proved quite irritating; the controversies over his medical theories were too numerous to be reckoned. But all of these objections were comparatively minor, and when some of the most distinguished scholars withdrew from his company and even showed aversion toward him, it had a more serious cause: the darkening clouds of suspicion of atheism which accumulated over Cardano's head during his middle years.

It is evidently impossible to deny or confirm that Cardano was a heretic, and we know nothing about the most crucial point, the charges and proofs brought against him at the trials of the inquisition. But nowhere in his works does he express opposition to the church or direct scepticism in regard to the Christian dogmas.

At times his statements border on indifference. In the Basel edition of *De Varietate,* the printer Henrik Petreius, as we mentioned before, inserted a statement hostile to the

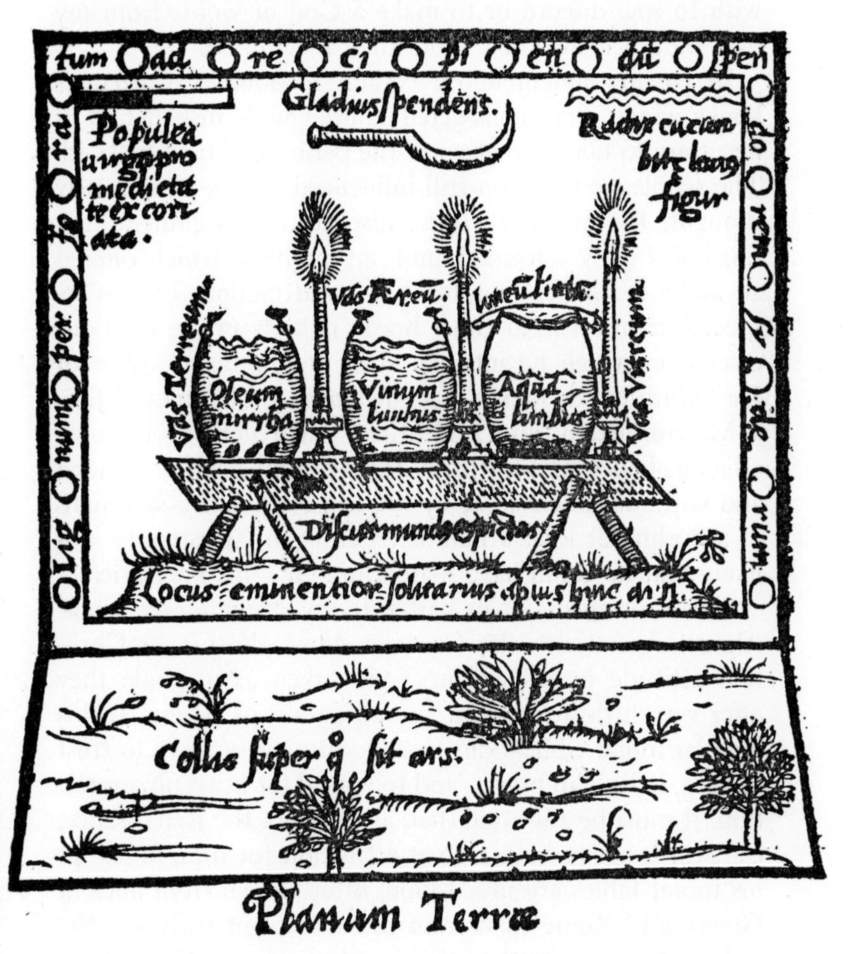

8. Cabalistic symbolism. From *De Rerum Varietate.*

Dominicans. In the corrected edition Cardano explains the situation and also expresses his own attitude toward religion as follows: "So far as regards my own way of life and my religion, I desire to follow that which is safest, to obey that law, and use those rites, ceremonies, and customs under which I was born and which have been obeyed and used for so many centuries by my forefathers. I have no wish to sow discord or to make a God of words from my own mouth or to know more than is required."

In passing judgment on certain sections of Cardano's books which were considered tainted with disbelief, it is necessary to take into account the period in which he lived. The scholastic tradition still influenced deeply all scholarly thought, the art of rhetoric, dispute, and argumentation was still highly esteemed, and any problem which offered an arena for logical combat had its attraction. In this respect Cardano was at times brash, notably in the fictitious discussion which he introduced in one of the chapters of *De Subtilitate* as taking place between a Christian, a Jew, a Mohammedan, and a Heathen. Each defends his own religious belief, and Cardano leaves the question undecided and without conclusions; by the usual scholastic safeguard of awarding at least a nominal victory to Christianity it is likely that he could have spared himself some later grief.

These instances, let us hasten to say, are rare exceptions. Almost everywhere else Cardano shows the proper Christian attitude in his writings, and taken as a whole they offer very little to support the allegation of heresy. In his popular moral edifications he advocates everywhere to trust in God, believe in prayer, and to appeal for heavenly protection. It must be admitted that, as a man of the Renaissance, classical learning held a great attraction for him, and thus his moral fables are much more often drawn from ancient Greece and Rome than from the Bible, but such was the style of his day. On the other hand, there are other studies which are devoted exclusively to Christian topics: he wrote a life of Christ and of the Holy Virgin, and studies on saints and many other sacred topics. In his book of counsel to his children he opens with precepts like these: "Give thanks to God daily when you can. You will become better by doing so. Speak of Him rarely, using his name only in reverence. When human efforts fail seek help from God."

In his *Autobiography* Cardano has a chapter on his piety and religious convictions. He recalls his childhood prayers, assures that he has always worshipped God and held to the tenets of the Catholic Church, although he is compelled to admit that on occasions he has been assailed by doubts. His tone is apologetic and the reason is evident. The trials of the inquisition were still freshly in his mind when his *Autobiography* was composed, and he had still not given up hope of obtaining a pardon to the extent that he might resume the publication of his books.

The Reformation never had any attraction to Cardano. Among the various reasons which he enumerates for his refusal to accept the distinguished offer from the Danish king to serve as his personal physician he mentions specifically that it would be repugnant to him to live in a country of heretics. Before his audience with the king of England, Cardano was instructed to begin by addressing him with his full title, including "Defender of the Faith"; and when Cardano refused, the royal gift, according to his account, was reduced from one thousand crowns to one hundred crowns. He cast the horoscope of Martin Luther only to find an occasion to be critical; it was based upon incorrect data, as it was pointed out later, and the error may well have been intentional.

Among his best-read books are those containing reflections on popular philosophy, ethics, and morals. They are full of admonitions; sometimes one finds deep and touching thoughts or common sense expressed in pithy language, but Cardano also stoops to platitudes and superficialities. His illustrations are drawn preferably from his own life and family, or from classical authors. Let us quote a few of his utterances from the 1683 English translation of *Consolation.*

"It is also to be remembered that time is a medicine for

all manner of troubles. Who grieves for his grandmother that died four-score years ago? Or goods lost thirty years since? Such is the nature of time that, first, it lessens our extreme sorrow or joy, secondly, wears out our affections,

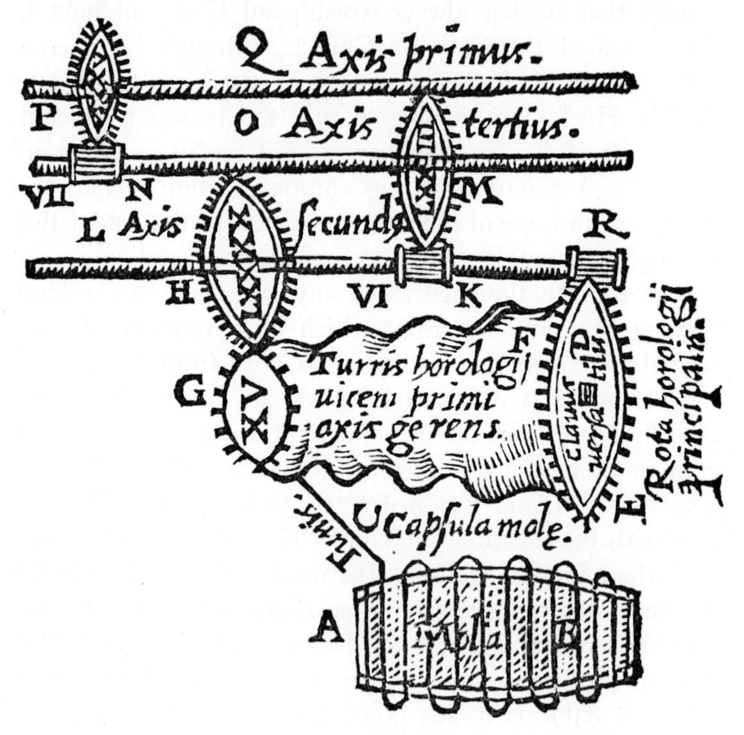

9. Cardano's studies on clockworks. From *De Rerum Varietate.*

and lastly, works in us forgetfulness of that which is past. Why can we not have enough influence over ourselves so that we may effect a speedy cure? It is a great argument of wisdom to bear with patience immediately that which others cannot until a great deal of time be past.

"Nor does sorrow serve any other end than to increase our cares and render our minds more inept for counsel. Continual grief will drive us ultimately to desperation. Then, since it is in our own power to aggravate or diminish our cares, it is the part of a wise man to unburden himself of sorrow and to bear patiently whatever happens.

"A man's unfortunate days once past, he lives the rest of his life with greater delight. Who can relish health that has never been sick? Who knows the sweetness of his own country so well as he that has been long abroad? Or who can take pleasure in riches as he that has been poor? As salt savors meat so does past misery render our lives more pleasant.

"There is nothing that brings greater sorrow with it than joy, for pleasure when gone is succeeded by sadness. What do we live for? To eat and drink and talk of news and do the same things over and over again? What is there in life that can delight? Daily trouble to dress and undress oneself? Whereas the dead feel neither cold in winter nor heat in summer, cares and fears come not near them, for in the grave the wicked cease from troubling, and the weary may be at rest."

Many serious reproaches have been leveled against Cardano for his beliefs in all things supernatural. Whenever evil events were approaching, he had premonitions. He protected himself against harm through amulets and precious stones with mystical powers. He saw apparitions and visions of demons; one might say to excuse him that they seem to have come mainly in his dreams or when half-awake. He believed, as his father had done before him, that he was being watched over by a personal benevolent and protective genius who sounded warnings to him, made noises, knocked on doors, tapped on walls, or shook the buildings in which he slept. He was convinced that on some occasions his life had been saved by its intervention. At times a voice spoke to him, and Cardano recorded at length some of his conversations with the spirit.

In the face of such tales it is no wonder that some of his contemporaries believed that he was not in his right mind; some did not hesitate to express such impressions plainly and publicly. This question of Cardano's sanity has occupied many of his biographers; the evidence has been weighed by a number of physicians, and psychiatrists have even attempted diagnoses on the basis of the symptoms Cardano describes.

This is again one of the peculiarities of Cardano's character on which every conclusion must necessarily be conjectural. In studying his life and writings in some detail it seems difficult to find any convincing argument for a verdict of insanity, except possibly during the final period of his life when fate staggered him with heavy blows—the torture and execution of his son, his humiliation in recanting his "heresies," the loss of position and right to publish, the exile in Rome. But in full manhood, during the middle years of his life, he was an eminently successful writer, and distinguished men were proud to count him among their friends. When he finally began to make money he managed his affairs well, and above all he was a very popular physician with a great and universally recognized reputation. There is no indication that his patients were ever scared away by any abnormal behavior.

It must readily be admitted that Cardano was superstitious, but so was almost everyone else at this time. The highest arbiter of faith, the Church, officially recognized demons, spirits, and witches as dangerous phenomena. Beliefs in such beings might have been scorned by a few, but they belonged to the folklore of the many. Perhaps Cardano was preconditioned for some of these ideas. He was brought up in an unusually superstitious household and his father had always urged him to watch for signs and portents. That, and his vivid imagination and easy pen, may have prodded him into some of his fantastic descriptions.

In Cardano's later years it appears more likely that he suffered in some degree from senile dementia aggravated by loneliness and sorrows. In the *Autobiography* the supernatural accounts are much more prominent than in his earlier writings. In his preoccupation with the past Cardano meditated upon his misfortunes and wrote verses to his lamented son. Perhaps he had failed in not understanding the signs of his spirit. He relates that, although he had long been aware of the existence of his genius, it was not until he was seventy-four years of age and had undertaken

10. Amulet in the image of Emperor Alba belonging to Cardano. It was supposed to cure insomnia. From *De Subtilitate.*

to write the story of his life that he felt he could discern the principles upon which it had acted.

Cardano was intensely occupied with divination and all kinds of occult learning. At present it might be difficult to see how such an interest could be reconciled with an eminent scientific mind, but Cardano appears to have been quite convinced. He did not seem to find any inconsistencies in his own views, although at times he did make sceptical remarks on the use of such methods. Besides, Cardano was not the only great man who had difficulties in separating the chaff from the wheat in the mass of unorganized knowledge which was the legacy of medieval scholarship.

Among his notable contributions in the occult was a work of thirteen books on metoposcopy, a type of divination of which Cardano has sometimes been claimed the inventor.

Briefly, it concerns the study of character and future fate deduced from a man's face, the lines on his forehead, and other signs. Warts carried a particularly sinister portent: for instance, "a woman with a wart upon her left cheek, a little to the left of the dimple, will eventually be poisoned by her husband." Cardano's book is richly illustrated and contains a strange assortment of faces. But yesterday's

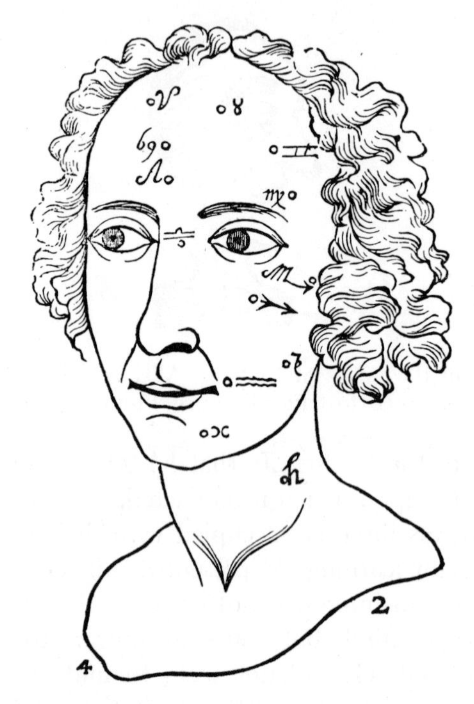

11. An illustration of divination from the position of warts. From Cardano's physiognomical studies.

superstition may be today's science. It has been maintained in all seriousness that Cardano should be counted as one of the forerunners of Lombroso's psychiatric theories about criminal types.

Cardano wrote on other kinds of divination: for instance, on chiromancy or palmistry as well as a book on predictions from thundershowers. He was well acquainted with geomancy, another prevalent method of predicting the future. Originally it consisted in examining the figures formed by sand or soil when scattered upon a board, not unlike tea-leaf reading. Sometimes a horoscope pattern was used as the basis. Later it seems that one should make marks at random for the geomancer to study.

In view of all this it is quite surprising that Cardano in his *Autobiography* denies ever having cultivated such fields. Since the facts are indisputable from his books, it can only serve to demonstrate again the apologetic character of some parts of *De Propria Vita.*

"But I have not applied myself to any malicious, dangerous, or vain sciences, consequently not to chiromancy, nor to chemistry, nor the science of poisons. I have not devoted myself to physiognomical studies, a wide and very difficult field which requires a combination of excellent memory and keen perception, abilities which I do not believe I possess. I have not attempted that kind of magic which seeks by incantations to evoke demons or recall the souls of the dead."

This denial of black magic may perhaps be an indication that charges of this kind had been made against him during his trials. By chemistry Cardano may possibly mean alchemy, and this seems to have been a field which he left alone. Incidentally, he did not believe in witches since the reports on their exploits were too contrary to natural laws, and in confessions wrought by torture he did not place great faith, guided by his own sad experiences.

Cardano professes openly only one kind of divination, even in his later years. He was an expert astrologer, an art in which he also had been instructed by his father. There was still no stigma attached to astrology; it was considered to be more of an exact than an occult science. Anyone with mathematical and astronomical learning was expected to cast horoscopes and many of the most prominent as-

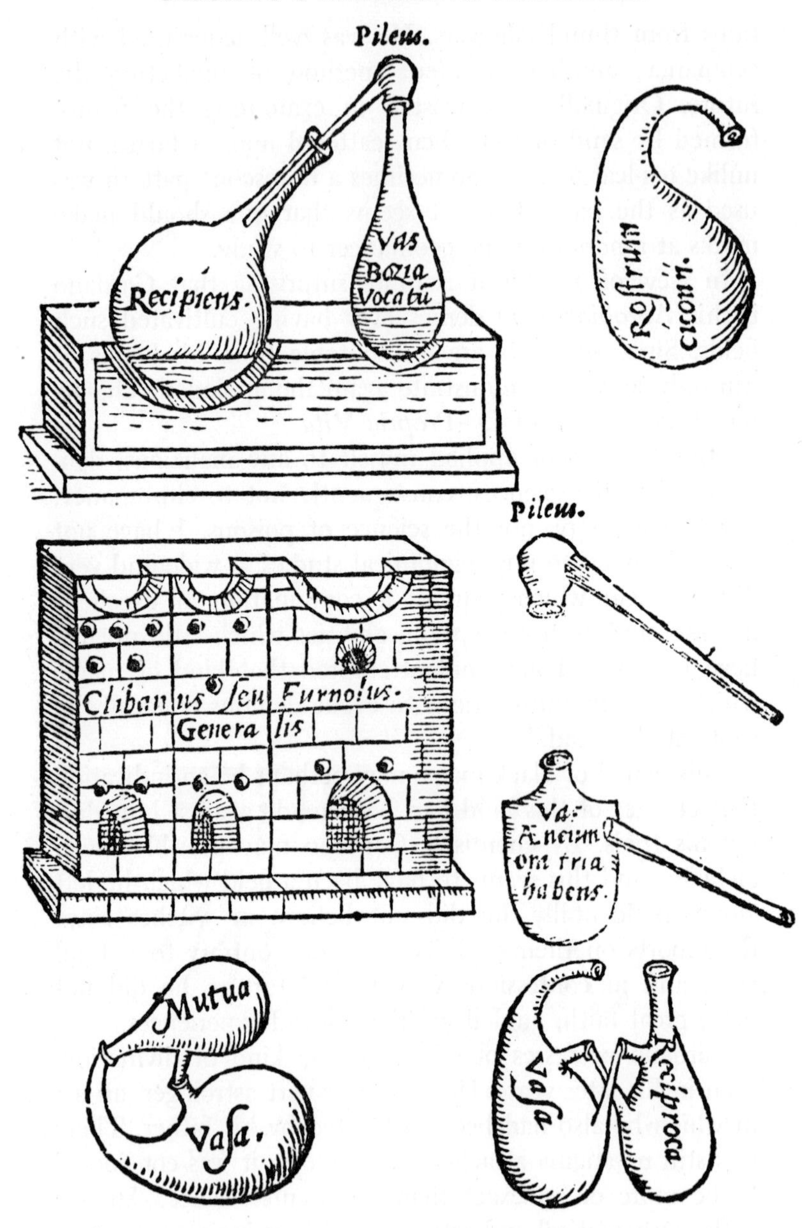

12. Furnace and chemistry vessels for distillation. From *De Subtilitate.*

tronomers earned their way by acting as court astrologers to their protectors. Cardano also added to his income by casting horoscopes, and as usual he wrote books on the subject, containing forecasts for hundreds of friends and famous men. Some of his predictions could be interpreted as being fairly correct, but others were evidently grossly erroneous.

Most embarrassing was the horoscope which he cast for Edward VI, the boy king of England. He was sickly, and behind the scenes at court there were preparations and sharp intrigues among those who wished to usurp influence after his death. When Cardano passed through London on his return trip from Scotland, he was received in audience by the king. Cardano was very favorably impressed with the young man, who had read some of his books and asked intelligent questions on several points. Some courtiers requested a horoscope for the king and Cardano was unwise enough to comply. He predicted a long life and described diseases which would afflict him when he reached the ages of twenty-three, thirty-four, and fifty-five years. The king died shortly afterward, sixteen years old, and Cardano was chided so severely that he felt obliged to offer explanations in a little composition which he entitled, "What I thought of the matter afterward." Another signal failure, but of a more private character, was the horoscope of Aldo, his scoundrel son, for whom he predicted wealth, fame, and genius.

Criticism of Cardano for his superstitious writings does not seem to have been too severe during his own lifetime, but in the following century the existence of these books almost ruined his scientific reputation. To writers on superstitious lore there could be nothing more desirable than to render their own statements plausible by pointing to the fact that similar views had been propounded by one of the most eminent scholars and physicians of the sixteenth century. As a consequence there are few men whose names are mentioned and whose works are quoted more often than Cardano's in the books on divination and magic; indeed, one may still run across him in some of these publications, together with his contemporary fellow physicians, Paracelsus and Nostradamus. As the influence of the natural sciences grew stronger and a more critical attitude of the public became noticeable, such a reputation made him an easy target for defamation. Astrology also gradually lost its standing, and in the heated arguments about its validity Cardano's many horoscopes formed rich material for ridicule. Many of the comments upon Cardano in the seventeenth and eighteenth centuries show a hostile attitude; to a large extent this appears to be due to his occult studies.

When young Gerolamo was in his 'teens he experienced the death of a relative and good friend, Niccolò Cardano. The boy was grief stricken, but as such things usually go, after a time Niccolò became only a memory and the name was rarely mentioned in the household. This brought the youth to ponder upon the shortness of life and how insignificant a mark an individual leaves behind in the currents of the history of mankind. So intense were his reflections on this subject that he proceeded to formulate them in writing. This was his first composition, a treatise on the ways in which a man could immortalize his name.

Cardano often deprecates the search for fame as being vain, but all through his life and writings there runs a strong undercurrent of this desire to create for himself a permanent niche in history. He tries to analyze the nature of this wish in his *Autobiography* in the chapter, "Thoughts on how to perpetuate my name."

"The thought and wish to perpetuate my name presented itself to me long before I had any means to realize my desire. Life is twofold, as I clearly perceive, a material life which we share with animals and plants, and another, properly human life, desirous for honors and achievements.

For the first of these lives I was badly equipped and I had no desire for it. For the second I had but little to give me cause for hope. I was failing in wealth, power, health and vigor, family, personal ability; even my knowledge of the Latin language was deficient. I had few friends and my family was lowly and impoverished. But after some years a dream gave me hope of attaining this second life, and although I did not see how, I came nearer to it through some kind of miracle which finally gave me command of Latin. But reason again compelled me to admit that such thoughts were vain and still more so the hope of realizing it through a strong desire alone.

"I said to myself: how can you write a book that will be read? What glorious subject do you know so well that people shall want to read about it? Will your language and style be sufficiently attractive to the reader? But let us suppose that you have gained your readers: isn't it true that as time goes by, day by day, there is such an overproduction of books that they are soon looked upon with disdain and so your own books will fall into oblivion? Your books may last a few years. How many? One hundred, a thousand, ten thousand years? Does there exist an example of a book which has endured that long, only a single one among the thousands? They may perish—in the eternal cycle as the Academicians believe, or also, because everything which has a beginning must have an end—but, if it is true that they must disappear, what does it matter whether it takes place after ten days or after ten thousand myriads of years: one or the other counts nothing in comparison with eternity. Still, you as a writer will continue to be tormented by hope, tortured by fear, and exhausted by labor. The sweetness of life will be denied you. Oh, what a beautiful prospect!"

Cardano goes on to remember the snow of yesteryear, the greatness of Caesar, Alexander, Hannibal, the Roman

Empire, all of little concern at present. He then continues his self analysis:

"Thus it is not surprising that I also have been inflamed by this wish, but it is strange that I have continued to feel this way after having understood the things which I have just explained; nevertheless, the stupid desire has persisted. The plans of Caesar and other great men were silly, so my own desire for glory under all these adverse conditions was not only silly, but insane.

"However, I must say that I have never wished for reputation and honor for their own sake; on the contrary, I have been rather contemptuous of them. I would like to have people know that I have lived but not that they should know how I lived. In regard to posterity I realize full well how hidden it is and how little it may be foreseen. Therefore I have lived my own life as much as I could and in my hopes for the future have been rather indifferent to the present. To excuse my design it may be said that thus my name would survive for some time and after a fashion. This appears honorable even if I should be deceived in my hope, and if this desire is natural, it should also be praiseworthy."

After all this one may ask, how did Cardano succeed in his search for a public? One particular reader should suffice to make Cardano's name remembered for a long time: When Cardano's *Consolation* or *Comforte* was translated into English in 1573 in an edition dedicated to the Earl of Oxford, the lord chancellor, one of his readers is known to have been William Shakespeare. Several Shakespearean scholars have gone so far as to identify *Comforte* as the book which Hamlet is reading when he enters the stage before his famous soliloquy, "To be or not to be—." Hamlet's thoughts on death and slumber are believed to have been inspired by similar passages in *Comforte,* for instance: "Most assured, it is, that such sleeps are most sweet as be most sound, for those are the best where like unto dead men we dream nothing. The broken sleeps, the slumber and dreams full of visions, are commonly in them that have weak and sickly bodies."

Cardano had also hoped to write for a large audience. Few writers have had more books published. It is true that some of his special works may have been published at his own expense when he was an affluent and fashionable doctor, but several of his more popular works can be characterized as best sellers. Especially popular was the *Subtilitate*, which appeared in many editions and numerous new versions within a few years, some of them authorized by Cardano and others pirated by printers all over Europe. The fact that the book had been placed on the index of the Spanish Inquisition did not reduce its circulation.

But as Cardano foresaw, the life of most books is short, and after his death there was a rapid decline both in his personal fame and in the reading of his books. The savory literature of the seventeenth century had a new attraction which made Cardano's writings seem heavy and pedantic. To most modern readers Cardano's works are forgotten and even his name barely lives on. Only one book still survives and is republished and retranslated from time to time, *De Propria Vita*. It is recognized as a new departure in autobiography, a document of deep human value. The many well-known, self-laudatory, and boastful life stories from the Renaissance are excellent and interesting reading, but the old man's psychological analysis of himself, his reflections on the struggles and tragedies of a scholar's long life, often touch closer to the heart.

There remains the important question of Cardano's worth as a scholar and scientist. Did he make new discoveries which moved forward the frontiers of science? Were his contributions permanent and valuable additions to the store of learning? To give a fair and complete answer to these questions is again difficult, but here we are at least on somewhat firmer ground regarding the facts.

An evaluation of a man's work must necessarily depend to some extent on the perspective of the arbiter, and in the case of Cardano this has varied more than is usual. If one places great weight on a single passage, on a single sentence or two, then some truly remarkable ideas can be found in his works. Cardano expressed thoughts which seem to indicate that he had an understanding of the principles of evolution; he surmised that petrified shells indicated that the mountains once were covered by ocean, an idea which he may have borrowed from Leonardo da Vinci; he thought that heat is a fluid which fills bodies to a greater or lesser extent. He described many simple physical experiments, particularly in *De Subtilitate*; he depicted numerous devices and gadgets, most of them taken from other writers, but a few seem to be his own inventions. All this is quite interesting as an illustration of the state of the natural sciences in the sixteenth century. It was certainly entertaining to his readers, but from the point of view of scientific progress one cannot escape the impression that Cardano most of the time is impersonally related to this material: much of his knowledge is based upon speculation or second- or third-hand information rather than on his own experiences.

Cardano considered himself primarily to be a physician. The greater part of his works concern questions of medicine, and here he is in much closer contact with his topics. The bulk of his writings is so overwhelming that it may be said that a detailed analysis and evaluation of all his medical views still remains to be made. But a great number of writers on the history of medicine have indicated important observations and suggestions which made their initial appearance with Cardano.

It is often pointed out that he gave the first clinical description of the symptoms of typhus fever, which he calls

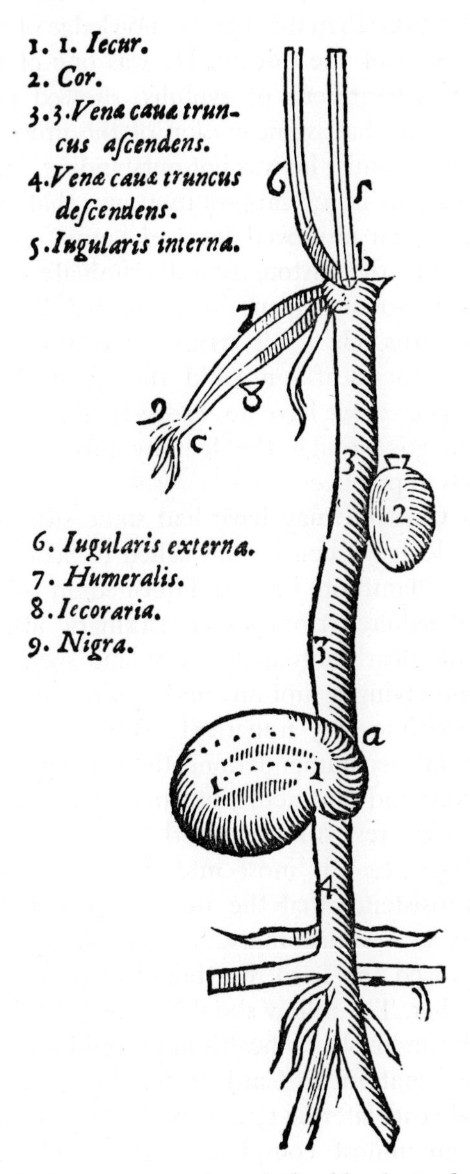

13. Cardano's conception of the blood circulation.

flea-bite fever, *morbus pulicaris,* rather because of the form of the skin lesions than due to any knowledge of the manner of transmission of the disease. He was one of the first to write on the treatment of syphilis, showed ability as a psychiatrist, and had some notion of the process of infection. As an anatomist he was not outstanding, but we know that he took part in several post-mortems, that as a surgeon he introduced an improved form of hernia operation and was opposed to the customary indiscriminate use of bloodletting. In personal hygiene he advocated the liberal use of shower baths. He made usable suggestions for the instruction of the deaf-mute and the blind. However, as could be expected, we have no reports that Cardano had the patience to go through the lengthy process of applying his methods in practice.

Perhaps Cardano may have had some suspicion of the causes of allergy. When he was called to Scotland to treat Archbishop Hamilton he was informed in advance that the patient suffered from severe asthmatic attacks which made his life nearly intolerable. Cardano spent more than a month observing symptoms and habits, and the prelate gradually became very impatient. When Cardano finally wrote out his recommendations they included some peculiar potions and ointments, but mainly they consisted of sensible advice: rest from overwork, sleep, diet, baths, and personal hygiene. But most interesting in this case was Cardano's insistence that the archbishop should not sleep on feathers as was customary, but on silk, and if one silk mattress proved too hard, he should place several on top of one another. The pillow should be made of linen, not of leather. The archbishop's health improved immediately and he remained grateful to Cardano for the remainder of his life. Several years later he sent a special messenger to Milan to report an almost complete recovery. The attacks of asthma now occurred only rarely, with intervals of months of relief. He again proffered his thanks and offered money or any other assistance of which Cardano might be in need.

In medicine Cardano must be counted as a member of the new school. He did not believe in the infallibility of the classical theories of Hippocrates and Galen and he rebelled against the authority of Aristotle. At times this led to violent opposition from some of his colleagues on the medical faculties and involved him in several public disputes. Cardano in one place expressed his views as follows: "I have been more aided by experience than by my own wisdom or by the faith in the power of my art." His emphasis on the psychic factor in health and disease has a quite modern ring: "A man is nothing but his mind; if that be out of order, all's amiss, and if that be well, all the rest is at ease." The following statement may easily make him a forerunner of the Coué method and other recent tendencies: "It was my design by my own example to teach these two things: first, it is nothing but a guilty conscience that can make a man miserable; secondly, constancy of mind helps greatly not only to bear evils but to produce a change of fortune. It is necessary to keep thee from being miserable to believe that thou art not so. Which rule, in one word, may be learned and taught by every man."

In one science Cardano's fame has been steadfast and secure: among mathematicians he will always remain one of the outstanding figures; in this field his creative genius won immediate acclaim.

A revolution took place in mathematics during the first half of the sixteenth century. The classical works of the Greek mathematicians had been for nearly two thousand years the unsurpassable pinnacles of mathematical attainment. And then, within a few years the shackles were broken and new fields with golden opportunities lay open. The theories of higher equations and algebra were created and some of the more visionary mathematicians, especially

Cardano, began to see the general principles which were to occupy mathematicians in the centuries to come.

This scientific explosion took place under circumstances which were peculiarly restricted as to time, place, and contributors. It all happened in northern Italy, at the University of Bologna and in the cities of Milan and Venice. The incidents surrounding the scientific discoveries, one of the most vivid and dramatic episodes in the history of mathematics, we shall relate in the following chapter. Let us only say here that the center of the controversy was Cardano's masterpiece, *The Great Art, Artis Magnae Sive de Regulis Algebraicis,* usually called briefly the *Ars Magna.*

The *Ars Magna* was printed in Nürnberg by Cardano's favorite printer, Petreius. It appeared in 1545, almost simultaneously with two other milestones in the history of science: Copernicus' book on the planetary system, *De Revolutionibus Orbium Coelestium,* and Vesalius' work on anatomy, *Fabrica Humani Corporis.* Cardano's book is as fundamental in mathematics as are the other two in astronomy and medicine. No one disputes Cardano's greatness in this work, but it may have a blemish; his rival Tartaglia accused him violently of having appropriated ideas of others for his own benefit.

The *Ars Magna* and his textbook on arithmetic were not Cardano's only mathematical contributions. He wrote other excellent works, some published and others found among his papers. Nevertheless, Cardano does not seem to have felt himself to be a mathematician; he was primarily a doctor and mathematics was more in the line of recreation. His favorite pupil Ferrari made the statement, "Signor Gerolamo has such skilful intelligence that not only in medicine, his profession, is he so proficient, as we know, but also in mathematics, which he sometimes uses to play with to relax and amuse himself, has he succeeded so well that speaking modestly he is considered to be one of the foremost mathematicians."

Cardano's many activities as we have described them may seem sufficient to keep any man extremely busy, yet he had at least two other great recreations, one a devotion to music and the other an obsession for gambling, card playing, and dicing which according to his own admission occupied him almost every day. Cardano would not have been true to his character had he failed to write learned books on

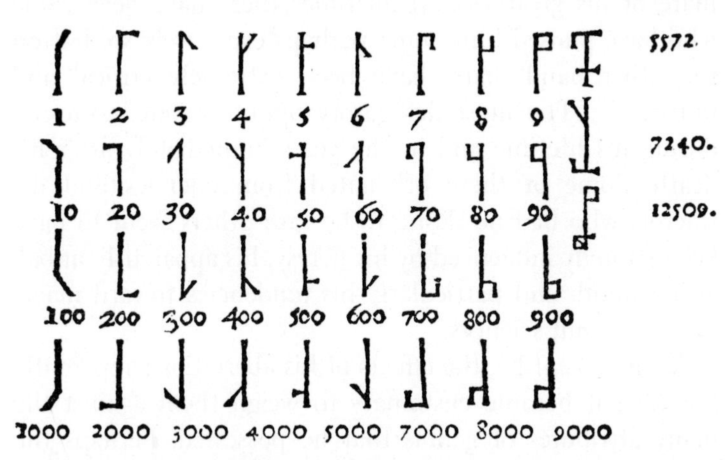

14. Cardano's proposal for a condensed system of writing numbers. From *De Subtilitate.*

these topics. His book on music is still extant, and in the description of his works he lists the manuscript in the category of mathematics, so evidently he considered it a very systematic work.

For his gambling Cardano has been much reproved by his biographers, who are quite in agreement with his own statement that gaming cost him time, money, and reputation. His book on gambling is an entertaining document as we shall see. But it is entirely in line with the bizarre twists of fate in Cardano's life that this vice alone would suffice to reserve him a prominent place in the history of science. His originality in other fields has sometimes been questioned, but *De Ludo Aleae,* his obscure and somewhat disreputable book on how to win at cards and in dice games, contains indisputable proofs of his genius. Whether one wants to call Cardano the inventor of the theory of probability, contrary to all present histories of science, or to name him its foremost pioneer is a matter of evaluation, but he is one of these two things.

Cardano's biographers have varied widely in their estimate of his greatness. At all times there have been some who have praised him, some perhaps excessively so, but on the other hand many have been extremely critical and unfriendly. The most derogatory opinions were expressed during his lifetime and in the years immediately after his death. Some of these originated from enemies and detractors who had no desire to be fair; others seem to have been strongly influenced by his heresy, his apparently unbalanced mind, and particularly his tendencies toward magic and the occult sciences.

As time went by, the effects of his aberrations apparently lessened; it became customary to weigh them against the many attributes of genius that he possessed. Perhaps the foreword to the reader in the 1683 English edition of *Consolation* expresses this sentiment sufficiently well.

"You have here an antidote against every trouble, prescribed by that physician whose prodigious parts and singular fancies have made him admired and envied by most of the learned world. He has (it is true) his *delirium* in common with all great wits, but his lucid intervals were such as made him pass, in the opinion of some that read his works, for *more* than a man."

Cardano's many peculiarities no longer seem to evoke any feelings of irritation in his recent biographers; they view them more charitably as eccentricities, or perhaps rather as human weaknesses which can largely be understood against the background of his education and his environment. His many good qualities stand out in clearer

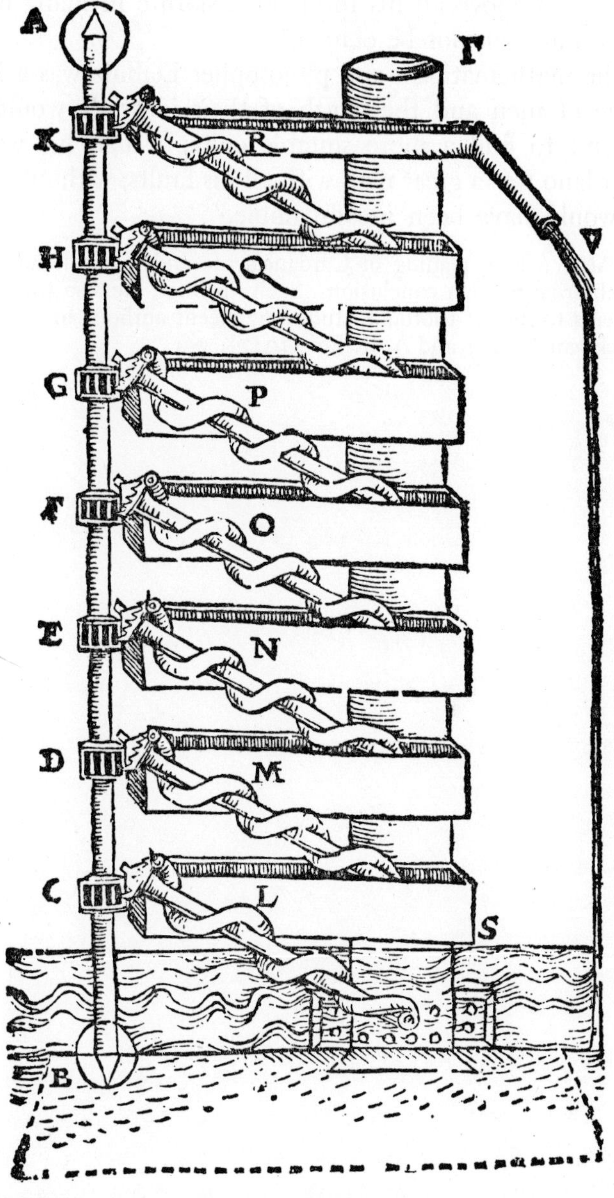

15. Multiple Archimedes screw for irrigation purposes. From *De Subtilitate.*

relief, and above all his formidable stature in many fields of learning can not be denied.*

The mathematician and philosopher Leibniz was a keen judge of men and the worth of their ideas. It would be difficult to find a more suitable epitaph than his words, "Cardano was a great man with all his faults; without them he would have been incomparable."

* After a long reading of Cardano's life and works I am ready to subscribe to such conclusions. Such, in brief, are also the views, it seems to me, of thorough studies by recent authors, for instance J. Eckman (1946) and A. Bellini (1947).

The Battles of the Scholars

THROUGHOUT his life Cardano was involved in controversies of one kind or another. Many of these were of the entirely normal kind expected of scholars in the sixteenth century, beginning with heated arguments regarding professional opinions, scientific views, or interpretations of the classical authors; after a period of acrimonious encounters they were usually resolved, in the tradition of the medieval universities, by a challenge to a public debate. If the opposing parties were of sufficient standing, the dispute took place before the authorities of the university and officially appointed judges. It was on the whole a gala occasion; each contestant appeared with his students and supporters and not only was public betting a part of the entertainment but the two disputants would often post sizeable amounts of money so that victory would bring gain as well as honor.

Cardano began his university disputes in his student days, apparently with much success; he continued in his more mature years and it seems that it was particularly his critical opinion of such classical medical sources as Hippocrates and Galen to which his colleagues took exception. Cardano must have been well equipped for the debates; he had a quick wit, a good memory, and a sharp tongue. According to his own account he became so proficient in these mental duels that his opponents had little chance of victory, or even defeat with honor. He shows no modesty in describing some of his exploits in the chapter of the *Autobiography* devoted to his teaching and disputes:

"In this field I was more arduous and successful. In Bologna I almost always lectured extemporaneously. No one dared to dispute with me. During the public dispute in Pavia against Camuzio, scheduled for three days in the presence of the senate of the university, he was reduced to silence not only the first day, but by my very first argument, as may be attested to by all those of my rivals who were present. There exists a printed account of it. Everybody recognized my victory so clearly that no one discussed the validity of my argument, but only talked about my invincible force. Branda, my teacher, mentioned before, attributed it to my superior ability and intelligence, while my rivals believed a demon had inspired me.

"Others saw the more reasonable explanation: during the past twenty-three years I had found no one, neither in Milan, Pavia, or Bologna, nor even in France or Germany, who would contradict me or dispute with me. I do not boast of this; had I been as dumb as a millstone the same thing would have happened. This does not stem from my superiority, but only from the blindness of those who wish to measure their wit against mine: it is exactly as when a cuttlefish envelops a dolphin with its dark fluid and causes it to flee; there is no glory to be ascribed to the cuttlefish, it is only its nature."

Among Cardano's scientific feuds there were two which aroused public interest to a high degree. In both one must admit that Cardano behaved with great candor and circumspection, and there is no doubt that in general opinion he was both times regarded as the winner.

The first of these encounters had a quite comical outcome. It began with a most violent attack upon Cardano by Julius Caesar Scaliger (1484-1558). Scaliger, nicknamed "the Terrible," was born in Italy but spent most of his life in France. Only quite late did he make his debut as an author, but gradually he acquired a considerable reputation as a writer on scientific and philosophical questions. In his youth he had served in the army of Emperor Maximilian and distinguished himself by his ferocious valor in combat. When he entered upon his literary career he seems to have believed that the way to make a name for himself was the same as in war: namely, to select the most distinguished opponent he could reach and slash him down in the shortest possible order. He began these tactics in a work against Erasmus, criticizing him vulgarly and most unjustly, but sometimes with a good deal of wit. The next victim on his list was Cardano and *De Subtilitate,* whose popularity had aroused Scaliger's ire. In a work of about twelve hundred pages he proceeded to tear Cardano's book to pieces. He abused and ridiculed it, pointed out error after error as well as calling it an abominable composition with an execrable Latin style. To make certain of having enough ammunition Scaliger based his attack on an early edition of *De Subtilitate,* although at this time there were available several new and improved versions corrected by Cardano himself.

Contrary to public expectation Cardano did not react very strongly. He had already had an overwhelming number of proofs of the success of the book and could afford to face an attack with indifference. But his opponent anxiously awaited a repartee, ready to begin his projected fray at the opponent's first counterblow. After many months of waiting, when no word had still been received from Italy, it seems that someone may have played a practical joke on Scaliger, or perhaps his sense of humor had deserted him and a word in jest had been taken too literally. Whatever the reason may have been, Scaliger gained the impression that Cardano was dead and the direct cause of his demise was his own unbridled assault.

This, certainly, was not according to Scaliger's plan. To have become the murderer of one of the most famous literary figures of the day reflected too seriously upon his own reputation, and so he immediately set out to remedy the situation as well as could be done by composing a grandiose eulogy over Cardano. This funeral oration is as lavish in its praise as the abuse had been previously:

"When the cruelty of fate had pressed on me so miserably that with my private glory was combined the bitter-

16. The Terrible Scaliger. From an old print.

ness of public grief, and my efforts so eminent and laborious were followed by a calamity so dire: I thought that I must not neglect to leave a testimony to posterity that the distress of mind occasioned to Hieronimus Cardanus by my trifling castigations was not greater than my sorrow at his death.

"For even if his life had been a terror to me, yet so great was his merit in all departments of letters, that I, who am but a citizen of the literary world, ought to have preferred the common good to my own personal convenience. For the republic of letters is bereft now of a great and incomparable man: and has endured a loss which perhaps no after-centuries may know how to repair. I, who am but a private man, have lost a witness and a judge, and even (immortal gods!) an applauder of my lucubrations: for he approved of them so much, that he rested all hope of his own defence on silence, despairing of his own power, ignorant of his own strength: for in strength and power he so much excelled, that there could escape his knowledge no possible way in which my castigations might have been turned to the increase of his own celebrity."

Scaliger goes on in this manner for several paragraphs, praising himself by praising the supposedly stricken Cardano, lamenting the great master who died of chagrin at the exposure of his errors. Finally he concludes:

"Wherefore, I lament my lot, since I had the clearest reasons for engaging in this struggle, the most explicit cause of conflict, but instead of the anticipated victory I obtained such a result as neither a steadfast man might hope (for who would have anticipated such an end to the affair?) or a strong man desire.

"My praise of this man can scarcely be called praise of an enemy. For I lament the loss suffered by the whole republic, the causes of which grief the herd of literary men may measure as they can, but they will not be measured in proportion to the merits of his real divineness. For whereas learned men ought to excel in three respects—in integrity, in erudition, and in wit joined to solidity of judgment—these three points so completely met in him, that he seemed to have been made at once by nature wholly for himself and solely for the world. For no man was more humane and courteous even to the lowest, no man was more ready for all dealings with the greatest men. Royal in lenity, popular in the elevation of his mind, he was the man not only suited for all hours, but also for all places, for all men, for all changes of fortune. Forasmuch as concerns his erudition, I ask you to look round on the most consummate world of letters in this happiest of ages; many and great men will display each his own merit, but each occupied only on this or that part of philosophy. He, however, so joined with the profoundest knowledge of the mysteries of nature and of God an acquaintance with humane letters, and expounded them with so much eloquence, that he appeared to have devoted his entire life to their study. Truly a great man, great if his power were not more than this. But if we consider the surprising swiftness of his wit, his power, as of fire, to master anything, embracing equally the least things and the greatest, his laborious industry and his unconquered perseverance, he may be called shameless who should venture to compare with him."*

However, Cardano was not dead; when Scaliger's publication reached Milan it must have been the occasion for much amusement. Later Cardano wrote a refutation of Scaliger in very moderate and sober terms, but he made it perfectly plain that he felt that Scaliger in his haste to point out faults had committed more errors than he had attempted to correct. Cardano did not even yield to his opponent the satisfaction of mentioning him by name; the retort is addressed quite abstractly—to a calumniator. In his systematic manner Cardano compiled in his *Autobiography* a long list of writers and works in which he had been praised and in this he included, quite properly, the name of Julius Caesar Scaliger; but to keep accounts balanced he also mentions him in the briefer list of those who had maligned him. However, Scaliger is not classified in the group of the worst detractors "for he only attacked me to acquire a reputation."

* H. Morley, *The Life of Girolamo Cardano of Milan, Physician*, 2 vols., London. 1854.

The mathematicians, as we have already said, held Cardano in high esteem, and Cardano's enumeration of his admirers includes a great number of them. But in the list there are two peculiar entries where Cardano takes a wholehearted slap at worthy writers. Both are mathematicians, one of them, number fourteen, "Borrel, a millstone around my neck who knows nothing and can learn nothing," and number sixty-six, "Niccolò Tartaglia, who after having slandered me was compelled to sing the hymn of the penitent." But these derogatory statements are not enough; both are placed in the group of the worst calumniators, and as Cardano observes, "among these I know no one who in his studies has passed beyond grammar school and I cannot see how they can have the audacity to count themselves among the scholars."

Jean Borrel (1492-1572) or Buteo, as Cardano calls him in the Latinized form, was a French cleric who had studied in Paris under Oronce Fine (1494-1555) or Orontius Fineus. Fine was by no means outstanding, but he was unquestionably the foremost among the French mathematicians. He kept an open house for prominent men at the court who dabbled in the sciences and was perhaps better known as a mapmaker and for his invention of a deck of heraldic playing cards than for his contributions to mathematics. Among other things he published a book in which he believed that he had discovered the quadrature of the circle.

When Cardano passed through Paris on his way to Scotland the French scientists and leading medical men celebrated his stay with banquets and meetings. Only the fashionable Fine was conspicuous by his absence. Cardano wanted to make his acquaintance and paid a courtesy call at his house, but Fine snubbed him by not returning the call. The reason for this animosity we do not know; it may have been caused by Cardano's peculiar writings or by criticisms of Fine's mathematical works. However, Fine never attacked Cardano publicly, but his pupil Jean Borrel took up the cudgel on his master's behalf. He wrote a book on arithmetic, somewhat similar to Cardano's text on the same topic, and in some sections he berates Cardano mercilessly, and as one must confess, with little justification. Cardano had some amusement problems based upon biblical themes, like the number of offspring of Adam and Eve or the time needed to build the tower of Babel, and these seem to have irritated Borrel especially. He said in plain words that they could only have been invented by an insane man. Cardano did not consider him an opponent of sufficient standing to be worthy of a reply.

In medicine Cardano had many competitors and rivals; in mathematics there was only one worthy of being taken seriously, Niccolò Tartaglia (1499-1557). Tartaglia was born in Brescia and from the very beginning came to know the vicissitudes of life. The family was poor; the father was a lowly mail rider named Fontana. In the year 1512 the town of Brescia was sacked by the French army under Gaston de Foix and a large part of the population was massacred. Young Niccolò barely escaped alive; his head was covered with gaping sabre wounds and his mouth was cut open so that he could only speak with difficulty. His mother's care saved him, but later in life he always wore a long beard to cover the monstrous scars. His impediment of speech gave him the nickname Tartaglia or Tartalea, the stutterer; this he accepted and used steadily.

Most of the information we have about Tartaglia stems from the biographical notes which he includes in his mathematical books and it may not always be entirely reliable. He had very little formal instruction and tells quite quaintly about his first experiences in school. His mother had barely managed to scrape together the money for the first instalment on the tuition for a course with a writing master, but the money gave out when he had reached the letter K and he was dropped from the class. So his schooling came to an end before "I could write the initial in my own name," as Niccolò puts it. However, he must have been an enterprising lad; he absconded with the schoolmaster's notes and completed the course on his own.

Most of Tartaglia's knowledge of mathematics and science was probably also acquired through self-study, but his autodidactic efforts were not always equally successful. His command of Latin, for instance, remained insufficient, and so, contrary to the scholastic tradition of his day he preferred to publish books in Italian, actually in Venetian dialect. Tartaglia settled in Venice where he made a living as a teacher of mathematics. He kept his name before the public by taking part in a great number of public disputes and challenge contests. The purses at times were considerable and he seems to have been very successful in these activities.

The most influential book in Italian mathematics at the end of the fifteenth century was *Summa de Arithmetica, Geometria, Proportioni e Proportionalità*, first printed in Venice in 1494. The author, Luca Pacioli or Fra Luca as he was commonly called, was an itinerant Franciscan who gave popular lectures on mathematics and the principles of perspective at various Italian universities. He could count a great number of the most prominent contemporary artists among his friends, including Leonardo da Vinci. The *Summa* according to present standards was not a scientific work and the contributions originating with the author are decidedly minor. Perhaps one could call it a compendium or an assortment of the main mathematical facts inherited from the Middle Ages and a good textbook, especially in computation and algebra. But it is notable historically in some respects; for instance, it is the first printed book to explain the rules of double entry bookkeeping. Perhaps it may also be worth mentioning that one of the most commonplace terms of modern civilization makes an innocuous debut, namely, the word million.

In his algebraic sections Fra Luca solves both those equations in which the quantity to be determined appears only in the first degree, and equations of second degree. All of this represents mathematical knowledge as old as the Babylonians. The unknown quantity to be found, the x which is being chased so anxiously and with such varying degree of success by school children all over the world today, was called the *cosa* or "thing" by the Italians. Thus in Europe algebra was long known as the "Cossick Art." The square of the *cosa* was the *census,* the third power was the *cube* as at present, while the fourth power was the *census of the census.*

Pacioli did not believe that any general method for solving equations of higher degree than the quadratic could be found and stated so plainly in his book. But it was not long afterward, probably sometime between the years 1500 and 1515, that his prediction was shattered by the invention of a method to solve equations which contain both the cosa and the cube, that is, the equation which we in modern algebraic language would write as $x^3 + ax = b$. The discoverer was Scipione del Ferro of whom we know very little except that for thirty years he was professor of mathematics at the University of Bologna. When he died in 1526 his papers came into the possession of his son-in-law, Annibale della Nave, who was appointed his successor at the university and taught mathematics there until 1550. Another who had been initiated in the secret of the cosa and the cube was one of del Ferro's pupils, a rather mediocre mathematician by the name of Antonio Maria Fiore, from Venice.

None of these men made any move to print or to publish the solution and one can make a good guess as to their reasons. At this time challenge disputes, often for considerable sums of money, were still almost the normal form of competition in the learned world; university appointments were mostly temporary and subject to renewal, and the decisions of the university senate were strongly influenced by the outcome of these contests. Thus the possession of a secret and powerful method for solving certain kinds of problems must have been a potent weapon in the struggle for survival in the republic of the learned. It was probably accepted as a natural and irreproachable procedure—we have no evidence to the contrary—to keep such discoveries in hidden reserve.

When printing became commonplace later in the sixteenth century this attitude changed gradually into the modern view that a scholar's principal road to recognition and reputation is through the publication of all his secrets, be they large or small—or, in some instances, even if they are not secrets at all. Perhaps it is not unfair to say that in his controversy with Cardano, Tartaglia represents the medieval attitude where a discovery was considered to be private property, while Cardano almost leans too far over to the other side in his belief that all his thoughts were so important to humanity that they deserved to be published.

After del Ferro's death in 1526 Fiore felt free to exploit the ideas of his teacher. At this time there must also have been some discussion of the cosa and the cube proposition elsewhere in Italy. Tartaglia wrote that as early as 1530 he received some problems of this kind from Zuanne de Tonini da Coi, a teacher of mathematics in his native town of Brescia. However, as it has been pointed out in a study by E. Bartolotti, the problems of da Coi are of a special type which does not require the general formula, and he makes it very plausible that a simple guessing method was used.

But in 1535 Tartaglia was challenged to a problem-solving contest by Fiore. There were to be thirty questions and the loser was to pay for a corresponding number of banquets for the winner and his friends. Tartaglia prepared a variety

17. The only known portrait of Niccolò Tartaglia. From *Quesiti et Inventioni Diverse.*

of problems, but Fiore had only one arrow to his bow—all his problems concerned the cosa and cube equation. Tartaglia was troubled and worked frantically. One sleepless night—Tartaglia gives the exact date, between February 12 and 13—shortly before the expiration of the allotted time, an inspiration came over him. He discovered the method and solved all thirty problems in short order. Fiore, recognized to be strong in calculation but weak in theory, had been unable to do much with Tartaglia's questions and was declared the loser. The honor alone was satisfaction enough to Tartaglia and he magnanimously renounced the prize; perhaps also the prospect of thirty banquets face to face with a sad loser may have been rather uninspiring to him.

Sometime afterward Cardano received a visit from da Coi, who told him about the contest and the existence of a rule for solving the cosa and cube equation. Cardano seems to have disliked da Coi, but he was greatly impressed with his information. He was at that time preparing his arithmetical text and evidently hoped that such a discovery could be included. In many respects he had already improved on Fra Luca's book, and a whole chapter was devoted to errors which he had found in the *Summa;* but until now he had accepted without question the statement that no general method could be found for the solution of higher degree equations.

Da Coi also related that he had urged Tartaglia to make the method public, but Tartaglia had waved the suggestion aside with the remark that he would write a book on it in his own good time. It is puzzling that at this time no one put pressure on Fiore to obtain the information; it is possible that he had been sworn to secrecy by his old teacher del Ferro.

Several years passed and Cardano probably made fruitless attempts to discover the method. Early in 1539 when his *Arithmetic* was nearly ready to go to press, he decided to approach Tartaglia and sent the bookseller Zuan Antonio da Bassano to Venice as an intermediary. Tartaglia later described the interview as follows:

"*Zuan Antonio.* Messer Niccolò, I have been directed to you by a worthy man, physician of Milan, named Messer Gerolamo Cardano, who is a very great mathematician and reads Euclid publicly in Milan. At present he is preparing for print one of his works, *The Practice of Arithmetic, Geometry, and Algebra,* which will be an excellent book. He has been informed that you have had a contest with Master Antonio Maria Fiore in which you agreed to propose thirty questions each. His Excellency has also heard that this Master Antonio Maria proposed all his thirty questions such that they led to the rule for the cosa and the cube equal to a number; furthermore, that you found this general rule and on the strength of it you solved all of the thirty problems in two hours' time.

"His Excellency begs you to be good enough to send him this rule which you have found and if it suits you he proposes to publish it under your name in his present work, but if you do not see fit that it should be published he will keep it secret.

"*Niccolò.* Tell his Excellency that he must pardon me, that when I publish my invention it will be in my own work and not in that of others, so that his Excellency must hold me excused.

"*Zuan Antonio.* In case you should not want to communicate your invention his Excellency requested me to pray that you at least give him the thirty problems proposed to you with your solutions and similarly also the thirty questions which were proposed by you.

"*Niccolò.* This I cannot do because as soon as he has one of these problems with its solution his Excellency will immediately understand the rule which I have discovered, from which many other rules can be derived."

The bookseller also brought some problems from Cardano concerning the cube and the cosa, but Tartaglia immediately recognized them to be problems proposed earlier by da Coi and became suspicious. Cardano seems to have wanted to convey the impression that he already knew how to solve them, but this Tartaglia doubted for good reasons:

"*Niccolò*. If he knew it I am sure that he would not go begging and seeking for it."

"*Zuan Antonio*. I do not know what to say in return because I do not understand these things, but if you should speak to him I believe that he will know what to reply. But let all these things pass. In order that my trip shall not have been entirely in vain give me at least the copy of the thirty questions which this Master Antonio Fiore proposed to you and if you could also give me a copy of your thirty questions you would do me a great favor.

"*Niccolò*. Although I do not have much time I shall give you a copy of his list but I cannot let you have mine since I don't even possess a copy myself and I cannot remember them exactly for they were all of different types. However, if you will go to the notary where they were deposited, he may be able to make a copy.

"*Zuan Antonio*. Please give me only his questions then."

Cardano, naturally, was displeased and offended and gave vent to his feelings in a very insulting letter.

"I am much surprised, my dear Master Niccolò, at the disagreeable reply which you have seen fit to give to the bookseller Zuan Antonio da Bassano when he asked you on my behalf to give the solution of seven or eight questions which I sent you as well as a copy of the questions exchanged between you and Master Antonio Maria Fiore with their solutions. You have thought it sufficient to send me only the thirty questions by Master Antonio Maria which in reality revert only to a single one, namely, the cube and the cosa equal to a number.

"It grieves me deeply that among the many other difficulties of our science we should also have to contend with the presumption and discourtesy of those who work with it. It seems that it is not unreasonable that laymen consider us to be reckoned as being next to the insane. I should like to save you from the illusion that you are the first man in the world, an illusion shared by Zuan da Coi, who afterward had to leave Milan in despair. I want to write to you amiably to dissolve the phantasy that you are so great. I will lovingly let you know even through your own words that in knowledge you are rather in the valley than near the summit of the mountain.

"However, you may be more expert in other things than you have shown in your reply. Let me inform you that I previously held you in good esteem, and as soon as your book on artillery appeared I bought the only two copies which Zuan Antonio had received, one I kept for myself and the other I presented to the Signor Marchese. Furthermore, I praised you greatly to the Signor Marchese, believing that you would appreciate this in a more courteous and gentlemanly manner than Master Zuan [da Coi] to whom you allege that you are so superior, but in fact there seems to be little difference between you. At least, you have not shown it.

"Now let us come to facts. I shall charge you on four important points.

"The first is, that my questions were actually not my own, but belonged to Master Zuan da Coi. It is almost as if you wish to say that there is no man in Milan capable of proposing such questions. My dear sir: the abilities of men are not recognized through their questions as you believe, but through their replies. This shows a grave presumption on your part. There are many in Milan who understand these things and I knew them before this Master Zuan could count on his ten fingers, that is, if he is as young as he claims he is."

Cardano continues to tear into his opponent in a similar vein and even offers a deposit of one-hundred scudi for a dispute in Milan or Venice. However, the missive did have some positive sides. About a year earlier Tartaglia had published his first work, *The New Science of Artillery*, one of the earliest treatises on ballistics. It is only a small book, extremely naive and imperfect in many respects, but it is notable as one of the first attempts to examine the laws of falling bodies without bowing to Aristotle's authority. More than half a century later Galileo's experiments in Pisa were to produce the first incisive progress, but evidently Renaissance scientists such as Tartaglia and Cardano had already begun speculating on the matter, although they were incapable of arriving at any exact formulations. One of Cardano's arguments in the letter is a perfectly justified criticism of some of the assumptions made by Tartaglia in his book on artillery.

"The fourth point is a manifest error in your book entitled *The New Science of Artillery*, where you say in the first book, fifth proposition, that no body of uniform weight can proceed some distance of time with simultaneous uniform and violent motion. This is most false and contrary to reason and our experience in nature. The argument which you use to prove it seems still more extraordinary than the answer you gave to the bookseller. Do you not understand that it is unsuitable? In falling an object moves with increasing velocity, while forward it moves with decreasing speed, as we see from our experience in throwing a stone. When it descends it comes faster and faster toward the earth while forward it goes slower and slower. From your conclusion you draw many very peculiar consequences, but you should remember that clear-thinking men cannot be deceived so easily. I may be forgiven for correcting you in the discussion of artillery since this is not your specialty, but when I state that you have exerted yourself and succeeded in saying something noteworthy, you should not for this reason be led to believe that I am of the same calibre as you and Master Zuan da Coi."

To conclude Cardano proposes two problems; the second again leads to the ever-present problem of the third degree equation:

"Two men go into business together and have an unknown capital. Their gain is equal to the cube of the tenth part of their capital. If they had made three ducats less, they would have gained an amount exactly equal to their capital. What was the capital and their profit?"

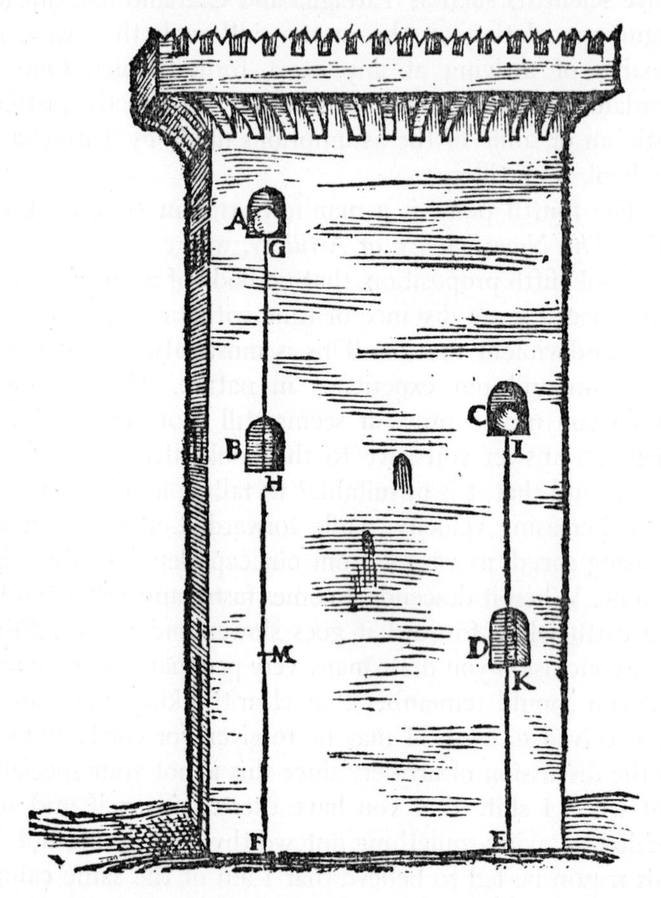

18. Study of fall motion. From Tartaglia's *La Nuova Scientia.*

Tartaglia was not to be trapped so easily, and in his return letter he solves the first problem, but as for the second he comments, "I have laughed greatly because I see that his Excellency wants to play *trappola* or perhaps rather *corrigiola** with me." Tartaglia complains about Cardano's "boastful, arrogant, and injurious words," but the tone of the correspondence is markedly changed. He admits that some of their differences may have been due to misunderstandings, and the plan for a public challenge is dropped altogether.

Tartaglia must have realized that a friendship with Cardano could be most advantageous. The Signor Marchese to whom Cardano referred was one of his good friends and protectors. He was Alfonso d'Avalos, marchese del Vasto, the Spanish governor of Lombardy and commander of the imperial army stationed near Milan, thus one of the most powerful men in Italy. He had a reputation for being an unusually generous patron and Cardano had made great efforts to win his favor; one of his books was dedicated to d'Avalos. Through Cardano, Tartaglia could be introduced to the Milanese court and would have a chance to explain in person to the governor his inventions in artillery and possibly to obtain a well-paid position as a technical expert. He sent two of his instruments to Milan, one a cannon sight and the other an instrument to determine target distances.

Tartaglia's defense of the principle of motion stated in his book is worded bravely, but otherwise it does not seem much to the point:

"In regard to this fourth charge of yours I reply that the reasons and arguments which you bring forth to destroy my fifth proposition are so weak and badly connected that

* The trappola or little trap was a common card game while the corrigiola was a simple-minded cheating game which worked about as follows according to medieval descriptions: The deceiver would wind a length of cord loosely around a stick which he then held in his hands at both ends. The victim was supposed to take the loose ends of the cord and guess in advance whether, when pulled, it would be outside or inside the circle formed by the stick and the arms. By releasing the loop suitably, the cheat could achieve any result he might desire.

an infirm woman would suffice to knock them to pieces. If the conclusion in my fifth proposition should be false, its first principles would be erroneous also. If this is so, it should be familiar to you that it is the duty of a capable doctor to investigate with the utmost diligence the principal cause of all defects which appear and when he has discovered it he should seek to remedy or cure according to the best of his ability because once the cause is removed all its sad effects will also of necessity be eliminated.

"Therefore, if your Excellency wants to oppose or argue against my fifth proposition, you should first of all criticize the true premises or first principles from which I concluded this proposition—as being the foundation and principal cause of this effect—because if you had been able to destroy the basis through some sophisticated reasoning of yours the whole building would have collapsed. But, in believing that you can demonstrate miraculously by your ridiculous opposition that I am wrong, you have only demonstrated, I will not say, that you are a great ignoramus, but that you are a person of poor judgment.

"Your Excellency also remarks that he excuses me for discussing artillery since that is not my subject, although I have succeeded in saying something ingenious about it. On this point I reply that I take delight in new inventions and treating new things which others have not discussed, and it does not please me to proceed as certain others who fill up their volumes with material stolen from this or that author. While talking about artillery and how to aim it at a target may not in itself be a very honorable matter, nevertheless, since it is a new topic not without speculation, it appears to me to be worth discussing a little.

"In this connection I will mention that I have brought forth two kinds of instruments useful in this art: namely, a square to aim the said artillery, to place it at level or to examine any elevation; the other, an instrument for the purpose of determining distances in the plane. It was planned that these instruments should accompany my book, and since you have written that you have bought two copies, having given one to the Signor Marchese and kept

19. Tartaglia's instrument for determining distances. From *La Nuova Scientia.*

one for yourself, I shall send you four of these instruments. They have been entrusted to the care of Master Ottaviano Scotto, who will transport them to you as soon as he obtains a messenger going in your direction. Two of these four instruments you are to give to his Excellency the Signor Marchese, and you should keep the other two for yourself."

Cardano answered these advances with sweetness and amiability on March 13, 1539:

"My dear Master Niccolò. I have received your very long letter which pleased me more the further I read; I wish it had been twice as long. You should not imagine that my sharp words were caused by enmity for there was no cause for that, nor from any evil nature, since I am much more inclined toward the good than the evil as the exercise of my profession, that is, healing, should cause me to be. Nor am I moved by envy to decide whether you are my equal or inferior, and should you surpass me in this art I should try to soar to your heights and not speak evil. Furthermore, the envious talk behind your back, not to your face.

"I really wrote that abuse to excite you to a reply, perhaps underrating your intellect from comparison with Zuan da Coi, who was here. I was friendly toward him and assisted him as well as I could, so you see I thought well of you and even had in mind to write you a letter at that time. But then he behaved most ungratefully, talked slanderously of me both privately and publicly; he challenged me in letters and with placards, but he did not succeed as he would have liked to. Three of his solutions in the contest, one from Euclid, one from Ptolemy, and one from Geber, were so confused that he parted in despair, leaving behind a school of about sixty pupils, which made me very sorry.

"If I have written you sharply I have done so on purpose, expecting to produce exactly what happened, namely, to have received your reply as well as the friendship of a man who is so singularly skilled in this art, as I can judge by the things you have expressed in your letter. Thus I have committed a sin which I am reluctant to repent."

The letter touches only lightly upon their various arguments and suggests that they talk over their scientific problems at leisure when they meet personally.

"I informed the Signor Marchese about the instruments which you have shipped, although at present they have still not arrived. I also told him about the lecture announcement, and all these matters pleased him greatly. He asked me to write this letter to you, with great urgency and in his name, requesting you to come to Milan as soon as you have received it so that he can discuss these matters with you. I advise you strongly to come immediately and not to procrastinate. The Signor Marchese rewards men of genius so generously, he is so liberal and magnanimous, that no person who has served his Excellency in any capacity has been dissatisfied.

"So do not hesitate to come and stay in my house. That is all. Christ protect you from harm."

"In this way," Tartaglia commented, "I have been placed in a peculiar position, for if I do not go to Milan the Signor Marchese will be offended and this might cause me harm. I shall go there most unwillingly; however, I shall have to go."

The principal points of Tartaglia's whole story seem to be trustworthy and the account of his subsequent visit to Milan is probably equally acceptable. But it should not be forgotten that it was all composed many years after the event and written at a moment when Tartaglia was in a white rage over the injustices he felt that he had suffered. It is evidently somewhat flavored by his animosity and also by the universal human weakness of presenting one's own role in the most favorable light. In the subsequent public feud Cardano's pupil Ferrari openly charged that the correspondence had been altered; however, we have no other sources for these events.

Tartaglia unfortunately arrived at a time when d'Avalos was absent at the castle of Vigevano, some distance outside of Milan. He spent three days waiting for the governor's return and in the meanwhile Cardano must have been at his best as a pleasant host. Tartaglia reported their conversations in the form of a dramatized dialogue taking place on March 25, 1539. Naturally the question of the solution of the cosa and the cube was on the agenda again

20. Tartaglia's instrument for measuring elevation. From *La Nuova Scientia.*

and Tartaglia insisted as before that he wished to publish the result himself. Cardano attempted a counterproposal, suggesting that it be included in a separate chapter in his book under Tartaglia's name and announcing him as the discoverer. Even this compromise was not acceptable to Tartaglia, but after a while he finally decided to divulge the secret provided that Cardano would swear solemnly never to reveal it. To this Cardano agreed and took the following oath, according to Tartaglia's version:

"I swear to you by the Sacred Gospel, and on my faith as a gentleman, not only never to publish your discoveries, if you tell them to me, but I also promise and pledge my faith as a true Christian to put them down in cipher so that after my death no one shall be able to understand them."

Cardano said after this that, if Tartaglia did not believe him now, there was not much he could do about it, and Tartaglia admitted that, if he did not have faith in such an oath, there was not much he could believe in in this world. He produced a paper on which the solution was written down in the form of a long and cumbersome poem, a sort of semicipher, and presented it to Cardano. Then he took his leave, saying that he intended to travel to Vigevano to meet the governor; Cardano gave him a letter of introduction and off he trotted.

No sooner had Tartaglia left Cardano's street before he turned his horse in the other direction, homeward toward Venice. He was already beginning to regret his momentary weakness, and he had had enough of Milan. But only a short time after his return another friendly letter from Cardano arrived saying that his book was now practically completed, but complaining also that there was an obscure point in the poem on the equation. He was surprised that Tartaglia had left Milan so hurriedly without seeing d'Avalos, who had returned to Milan on Easter Sunday. Cardano had spent an evening with him a few days later and discussed the instruments with him in some detail, and the marquis had realized their usefulness. "The time may still come when you may be glad to know the Lord Marquis. If you would let me know why you left or by whom you were advised to do so I shall explain the situation to him."

It has been charged that Cardano only pretended these

arrangements with d'Avalos for the sole purpose of using them as a bait to attract Tartaglia to Milan; the whole correspondence should have been built up with this climax in view, but this seems a most improbable conjecture. Others, consequently, have vehemently denied such accusations, pointing out that it was an extremely natural development, that Tartaglia was most anxious to come and made every possible move to obtain the invitation. It is evident that, had it all been based upon deceit, it would have been a very complicated and dangerous scheme. The ruse could readily have backfired if Tartaglia on the strength of the invitation had written directly to d'Avalos. Furthermore, under such circumstances it would have been quite senseless for Cardano to continue to impress Tartaglia with the possibility of favors from the governor after the secret had been divulged. Even the suspicious Tartaglia nowhere insinuates foul play on this point. The ensuing correspondence indicates quite clearly that Cardano, in spite of Tartaglia's animosity, makes every effort to preserve friendly relations. In the *Autobiography* he also observes regretfully that Tartaglia preferred to have him as a rival and superior rather than a grateful friend.

Tartaglia in his reply clarifies the point which Cardano had mentioned, but he drops all pretense of friendliness, even the customary amenities of address. He states that he is very anxious to see the *Arithmetic* so that he may be reassured on his suspicion that the rule could have been inserted in some part of the book.

The *Practica Arithmeticae Generalis* appeared in May 1539, and Cardano hurried a copy, still wet and unbound, to Venice to relieve Tartaglia's mind. With the sheets he dispatched a most courteous letter assuring him of his sincere friendship and that he had no intention of violating his oath. For a moment Tartaglia was at ease on this point, but he now had a foundation for mathematical attacks upon Cardano; he ridiculed him for the errors in the book, which one could discover with half an eye, and berated him for ignorance and plagiarism, all apparently for the sole pleasure of being unpleasant. But during the summer Tartaglia's anger and suspicions were fanned to a white heat again. A former pupil, Mafio, wrote to him that he had heard rumors from Milan to the effect that Cardano was writing another book on algebra. Mincing no words Tartaglia burst forth in his next letter: "I must say that I am very sorry that I have given you as much as I have already done, for I have been informed by a trustworthy person that you are about to publish another algebraic work and that you have been boasting in Milan that you have discovered new rules in algebra. But beware, for if you break your faith with me, I shall certainly not break my promise to you, for that is not my custom, but I shall retaliate with more than I promised."

Cardano replied politely, as always in this later correspondence, denying that he was writing a book on algebra and indicating that there must have been some confusion with another book, *Mysteries of Eternity*, which was nearly done. His statement was probably correct, since the *Ars Magna* was not completed until five years later, and it is not likely that he had begun composing it at this time.

The last letter from Cardano was written early in 1540 and here he complained again about this "diavulo de Messer Zuanne da Coi" who had made his appearance again in Milan. He had come upon a rumor that Cardano was about to resign part of his lectureship in mathematics, namely, those in arithmetic, and to qualify himself as a candidate he proposed various problems, some quite difficult, which Cardano forwarded to Tartaglia. Da Coi also made the disturbing assertion that he had studied the problems of Fiore in Venice, and after various conjectures he, as well as a companion, had finally found the rule of Tartaglia; Tartaglia's only comment was that he did not believe it. Da Coi's presence in Milan was evidently inopportune for Cardano since he had intended to resign for the express purpose of creating a position for his favorite pupil, Ferrari. But young Ferrari could well fend for himself; he defeated da Coi in a challenge contest and shortly after was confirmed in the lectureship.

Lodovico Ferrari (1522-1565) first came to Cardano on November 30, 1536, a red letter day in Cardano's life. "A magpie made such a loud and extraordinarily prolonged racket in the court yard that I understood that I could expect the arrival of someone." But the only visitors to the house were two teen-agers from Bologna, the fourteen-year-old Lodovico and his cousin, and Lodovico sought employment as a servant boy. "Was there any connection between the two happenings? Not at all. How many premonitions result in nothing? Some like Augustus, for instance, profited by such vague observations, while others like Caesar or Sulla suffered from not believing in them. It is almost as in dice games where there are no laws or at least these laws are fallible. But that which transcends nature does not belong to the field of rational reasoning, while that which is subject to nature holds no marvels except to those who are ignorant."

Cardano was soon to understand the sign of the magpie. The young Lodovico was able to read and write, and Cardano made him his secretary, instead of assigning him to menial tasks. He assisted Cardano with the manuscript for the *Arithmetic* and in the process absorbed the fundamentals of mathematics. It was soon evident that he was an extraordinarily gifted boy, and Cardano generously provided him with an excellent education. Lodovico on the other hand was a great admirer of his master and Cardano had no more loyal friend.

The information available about Lodovico Ferrari is scant and much of it must be culled from Cardano's works, particularly from the brief biography he wrote after his pupil's death. He was born in Bologna but the family was Milanese, the grandfather having been banned from Milan for some reason. The Renaissance abounds in impulsive and hotheaded geniuses and Ferrari ran true to form. He had such a temper that even Cardano at times was afraid to speak to him, and one day when he was seventeen years old he came home from a brawl missing the fingers on his right hand.

Before Ferrari's twentieth birthday he became public lecturer on his favorite subject, mathematics. His popularity and success were so great that among the numerous offers he received was an invitation from the emperor to be tutor for his son. However, Ferrari preferred a more active and remunerative position. He was appointed tax assessor by Ferrante Gonzaga, the successor to d'Avalos as Governor of Milan, but high living so aggravated a fistula he suffered from that he could no longer travel on horseback to supervise his surveyors; and so, in spite of the fact that he habitually deprecated the Church, he transferred to the service of Gonzaga's brother, the Cardinal of Mantua. He gradually accumulated a considerable fortune, and when he resigned after an altercation with the cardinal he retired in comfort to his native town of Bologna where he built a house and after a while was called to a professorship in mathematics.

Ferrari always remained faithful to his old master and on several occasions he was of assistance to him; it is likely that he was a strong supporter in the move to obtain an appointment for Cardano to the University of Bologna after the execution of his son. Unfortunately Ferrari died soon after Cardano's arrival at Bologna; according to unverified rumors he was poisoned by his sister or her lover. In his *Autobiography* Cardano lists three individuals as his foremost pupils and, incidentally, best friends: Gasparo Cardano, a relative, and Rodolfo Silvestri—both, as we have already mentioned, physicians and practitioners in Rome—

and the mathematician Lodovico Ferrari. Cardano concludes with a lament for Ferrari's premature death:

For those without measure life is short, rarely do
They attain old age. Whatever you may love or desire,
Let not your indulgence go beyond bounds.

Immediately after Cardano received the cubic solution from Tartaglia he began turning it over in his mind to examine the consequences. He had attempted to correspond with Tartaglia on these matters, but was rebuffed. Quite soon he must have succeeded in solving not only the cube and the cosa equation, but also the third degree equation in its most general form where all the powers of the unknown are present. He encountered the so-called irreducible case, the apparently so paradoxical situation where the formula gives expressions from which the roots cannot be extracted as ordinary numbers, yet in other ways one can find that there must be three perfectly good solutions. He realized that there always ought to exist three roots and so he was compelled to attack the calculation by using these imaginary numbers which ordinarily have no meaning. Assuming that they behave like other numbers in calculations, he arrived in the end at correct and intelligible results expressed in common numbers. At a time when even a subtracted and added term required study as separate cases and negative numbers were not yet fully understood, this handling of complex numbers, as we now call them, must have appeared as a piece of magic as mysterious as any of the occult studies in which Cardano indulged.

Cardano found methods for solving the equations by approximations and he had some ideas on the relations which connect the roots and the coefficients of the equation. In short, he had begun to wander around in the field which has later been given the name of higher algebra. To keep Tartaglia's formula a secret from Ferrari, a *famulus* and collaborator who lived in his own house and with whom he discussed mathematical problems every day, was obviously a physical impossibility. Ferrari, now approaching his twentieth birthday, in spite of his early years eagerly participated in these scientific voyages of discovery, and he soon began to add some contributions of his own; he discovered the method of solving equations of fourth degree which still bears his name. An enlarged circle of exploration had again been entered by the two pioneers.

So, master and pupil gradually accumulated a large body of new and important knowledge, all based on novel ideas, and unless their achievements were to be in vain, a way had to be found to make them public. The ominous obstacle, Cardano's oath, was both a moral obligation to himself as well as a solemnized contract which in the beliefs and customs of his times could not be disregarded without incurring the most severe censure. From Tartaglia no relief could be expected; he did not have the slightest thought of releasing Cardano from his promise. He had himself also made a promise, it is true, that he would publish his formula in a great work which he was preparing, but nothing was forthcoming and there was no use in asking for his intentions. If he replied, which was doubtful, it would as usual be an abusive letter, reaffirming only that he was biding his time.

It is a mystery why Tartaglia did not choose to publish his formula at this time; ten years passed between his discovery and its publication in the *Ars Magna*, and he ought to have been aware that his advantages were running out. Besides himself the secret was known to Cardano, Ferrari, Fiore, della Nave, and even that nuisance da Coi asserted that he had the method. Many others among the mathematicians knew the problem and public challenges had made it quite evident that a formula existed; any day an independent discoverer might have emerged. Tartaglia probably did not view the situation in such a detached manner; his foremost desire was to spite Cardano. Perhaps also he was stymied in his projected work by exactly those difficulties which Cardano had been able to conquer.

In the year 1543 Cardano decided to journey to Bologna in an attempt to confirm the rumors which were in circulation. He brought Ferrari with him so that he might have a mathematician as a reliable witness, and the two called at the house of their colleague Annibale della Nave. They were well received and readily given permission to examine the posthumous papers of Scipione del Ferro, and as della Nave well knew and as Cardano and Ferrari could now verify with their own eyes, here was explained the correct method for solving the cube and cosa problem.

Thus it was confirmed that Tartaglia was not the first discoverer; his secret was not only his own. The oath now also stood in a different light. To the medieval mind, as one sees from so many instances, an oath was only valid in its most literal sense and here was a circumstance which formally invalidated Cardano's commitment. Perhaps Cardano was still troubled by the moral obligation of his word as a gentleman to Tartaglia, but the impetuous Ferrari may have urged him on. The defense could be stated in few words: no oath to Tartaglia about his secret could deny him the right to use a discovery made by another many years before; the formula he made public was not the one stated by Tartaglia, it was the formula which belonged to del Ferro.

The *Ars Magna* appeared in 1545 and won immediate acclaim by all prominent mathematicians, except of course by Tartaglia. From the mathematical publications of the second half of the sixteenth century one can see that the book exerted a direct and profound influence upon the rise of European mathematics.

It is noteworthy that none of the contemporary mathematicians expressed the slightest reproach against Cardano in spite of the fact that the details of the affair were widely known and discussed; the castigation of his action began much later, principally by mathematical historians in the eighteenth and the beginning of the nineteenth centuries. In the form in which the result was published in the *Ars Magna* it is unquestionably not a theft of a scientific idea in the common sense; indeed, one may say that Cardano's statements are not far from being an acknowledgment which would be considered satisfactory under the circumstances in any scientific publication today. The chapter which deals with the method carries Tartaglia's name as a heading and begins with the information that the solution had been communicated to him by Tartaglia. But in the opening chapter the history of the discovery is related in more flowery detail:

"Scipione del Ferro, from Bologna, found in our time the rule for the cube and the cosa equal to a number, something truly beautiful and admirable.

"Such a discovery, a truly divine gift surpassing all human subtlety and the splendor of mortal ingenuity, is a proof of the virtue of the soul, a thing so marvelous that he who found it may have believed that there could be no difficulties he would not be able to surmount.

"Emulating this man, Niccolò Tartaglia from Brescia, our friend, who had entered into a contest with Antonio Maria Fiore, pupil of del Ferro, rediscovered this rule in order to win and he later confided it to me after I had made insistent requests.

"I had in fact been deceived by the words of Fra Luca who denied that there could exist general rules of this kind, beyond those he had given, and although the discovery could have been made easily from other things which I had found, naturally I despaired of finding that which I did not dare search for.

"After I was in possession of this rule and had found the proof for it, I understood that here many other things could be discovered, and with my confidence thus already increased I found such results, partly by myself and in part through the work of Lodovico Ferrari, my former pupil.

"All which has been discovered by these men will be designated by their name and that which is not attributed to others belongs to me."

Until the appearance of the *Ars Magna* the discord between Cardano and Tartaglia was of a private character, but from this point it became a combat before the eyes of all Italy. Tartaglia had promised retaliation and he so proceeded without a moment's hesitation. The very next year his book *New Problems and Inventions* appeared in Venice, strangely enough with a magnificent dedication to Henry VIII, King of England. It contained the solution to all those problems which through the years had been put to him by prominent men, at first questions on artillery and the making of gunpowder, but then almost exclusively mathematical problems. Tartaglia must have had his papers in remarkable order; the events are described in minute detail and the letters are quoted verbatim. The latter part is devoted exclusively to his dealings with Cardano; the exchange of letters is reproduced with Tartaglia's comments, the happenings at Cardano's house are vividly retold, and the oath is set down, word for word. Here, then, was a demonstration for all the world of the moral turpitude of Signor Gerolamo Cardano, physician in Milan.

Cardano never entered directly into the public phase of the feud, but his young adherent Ferrari upheld his colors with much skill and ferocity. On February 10, 1547, Ferrari issued his first challenge cartel, a manifesto in broadsheet form which was widely distributed and dispatched to scholars and high persons in the principal cities of Italy. It tears into Tartaglia with all the vigor of youth.

"There has come into my hands one of your books, entitled *New Problems and Inventions* and in the last part of this book you speak of the Honorable Signor Gerolamo Cardano, physician in Milan, who is at present public lecturer in medicine in Pavia. You have the infamy to say that he is ignorant in mathematics, a so uncultured man that even Giovan da Coi would be worthy of being placed ahead of him, and you call him simple minded, a man of low standing and coarse talk and other similar offending words too tedious to repeat. With these lies you attempt to convince the ignorant that your statements are true.

"I say the ignorant because I believe there is no person of any judgment who from the works he has published does not know him in a completely different light. By reading your nonsense one has the impression of reading the jokes of Piovano Arlotto, or I could say, Lucian's *True History*, were it not for the fact that you invent more ingeniously, have a better style and order, and use more flowery words.

"I really believe that you have done this in bad faith knowing full well that Signor Gerolamo has such a felicitous intelligence that he is known to be proficient not only in medicine, his profession, but also in mathematics, which he sometimes uses almost as a game for relaxation and solace. Here he has succeeded so well that speaking modestly he is known to be one of the foremost mathematicians.

"You hoped in this way, like the Homeromastix, to acquire a reputation and this is a laudable desire provided it is based upon your own ability and not upon defamation of others.

"Since his Excellency [Cardano] is prevented by the rank he holds, I have taken it upon myself to make known publicly your deceit or rather (as I believe) your malice, not only to defend the truth, but also because this matter concerns me personally since I am his creation [*che sono creato suo*]. This I shall do, not by returning word for word as I could, nor by words of others (as you) but by honest facts.

"Among the more than one thousand errors in your book I note first that in section eight you give a result by Giordano [Nemorarius] as your own, without mentioning him, and this is theft.

"You make up your proofs in your own head and thus they usually have no conclusion, but you have made the illustrious Signor Don Diego di Mendozza say things which I am certain—since I know at least part of his great knowledge—he would never have expressed for all the gold in the world. This is presumption and ignorance.

"But this is nothing when I consider that in the same book you dare to reprove Aristotle quite unjustly on his Mechanics.

"In the last section you repeat the same thing three or four times; this shows bad memory and negligence.

"However (as I said) I do not intend to attack you on these points (although I am ready to defend my charges).

"But I offer to dispute with you publicly on Geometry, Arithmetic and the disciplines which depend on them, such as Astrology, Music, Cosmography, Perspective, Architecture, and others. The contest may be held any place which is convenient to us both and before qualified judges. I accept to dispute not only on all that the Greek, Latin, and Italian authors have written on these topics, but also on your own discoveries which seem to please you so much, provided you will agree likewise to discuss my own.

"This I have proposed to make known, that you have written things which falsely and unworthily slander the above-mentioned Signor Gerolamo, compared to whom you are hardly worth mentioning. You presume to have reached some mark but you are much farther away from it than you think.

"What I did to Messer Giovan da Coi in 1540 is known to all, but you pretend to ignore it and want (as I said) to place him before Signor Cardano, whose name I mention so often with great respect.

"And so that you will not have to regret toil and expenses I propose to make a wager and deposit as much money as you wish, up to an amount of two hundred scudi, so that the winner may acquire the honor without loss and rather with advantage.

"Finally, in order that this may not appear as a private invitation I have sent a copy of the present pamphlet to each of the persons indicated on the following list, all of whom take delight in studying mathematics, and also to many others widely scattered in Italy and the provinces.

"I notify you that I expect an answer within thirty days after this has been presented to you. If this is not fulfilled I will let the world pass judgment upon your qualities. I reserve myself the right to proceed further if I should deem this desirable."

Then in the usual form follow the signatures of three witnesses and a list of fifty-three names of distinguished recipients.

Ferrari in reverence called himself "Cardano's creation." Tartaglia seized upon the double entendre, and in his later writings when he had occasion to mention Ferrari he almost always referred to him as "Cardano's creature." Ferrari, who had the very rare gift of gratitude, did not seem to mind; he took it as a compliment rather than as an insult.

In the first riposte Tartaglia countered from Venice on February 19, 1547.

"Excellent Messer Lodovico: On the thirteenth of this month I received one of your cartels printed in Milan on the tenth of the present. It was delivered to me by the honorable Ottavanio Scotto [Cardano's printer and university friend] on your behalf and he informed me that he had an infinity of others to be sent all over Italy. You send me at the same time, at the end of your cartel, the names of various gentleman familiar with mathematics in Rome, Venice, Milan, Florence, Ferrara, Bologna, Salerno, Padua, Pavia, Pisa and Verona, altogether fifty-three of them, and you hope by this action to scare me completely. But you are greatly mistaken, for I swear and affirm to you on my

Christian faith that since I was born nothing ever happened to me that delighted and pleased me more.

"To this cartel of yours I shall only reply on the principal points or proposals and to these only I shall give resolute answers. Should I react or reply to all your injurious, calumnious, and sharp words it would be necessary for me to fill a whole ream of paper. But since any document which is too long usually only produces confusion and tires the reader, this does not appeal to me. But I reserve the right to return to these particulars at any time I may see fit."

Tartaglia then almost literally repeated the various charges and the conditions for the dispute as offered by Ferrari and continued:

"To this cartel or proposal of yours I shall reply that there are two reasons why I have narrated in my book the details concerning Gerolamo Cardano.

"First, that I shall not break my word in the promise which I have made to his Excellency under oath, because I truly do not know any greater infamy than to break an oath, and this holds not only in our own, but in any other religion.

"Secondly, I have expressed this in such calumnious and sharp words to incite his Excellency, and not you, to write me in his own hand. I have many accounts to settle with him, but it does not suit me to tell them at present. But the same procedure [of producing a reply by insolence] was also used against me at one time (as it appears in the first letter which he wrote to me on Feb. 12, 1539, given in question thirty-two in my book). He writes me through a bookseller envoy that I have shown myself to be a great ignoramus, that I was too presumptuous and many other calumnies and his Excellency affirms in his second letter to have said these things to incite me to write to him. From this I infer that it has become the customary manner between us to incite the correspondence.

"Therefore, I say to you that if you have written this

cartel on your own initiative and not after coercion by his Excellency (a thing which I do not believe) I shall advise you in a brotherly manner to tend to your own lectures and leave such enterprises to the excellent Signor Gerolamo who is a man, as I believe you know, who would have replied himself if I had used any unreasonable words against him.

"But if his Excellency has provoked you to this, as I believe, then you should tell him from me either to write me personally or have somebody write for him in his words and not yours, in his name and not in yours, and when this is done I shall give him a suitable reply.

"You may say that it has pleased his Excellency to proceed in the manner done.

"And I reply that it does not please me to proceed in this way, namely, to reply to you, his creature, and not to him, since I do not desire to have anything to do with you, but only with him.

"You may say that at present his Excellency is not in Milan, but in Pavia.

"And I reply that at present I also am not in Brescia, my native town, but in Venice.

"You may say that his Excellency is occupied with his public lecture in Pavia.

"And I shall reply that, if his Excellency is occupied, I am also not idle, furthermore, if his Excellency is occupied with one lecture a day, I have at least fifty and nevertheless, if it is necessary I neglect them all, because when honor is involved it appears to me that it must be given preference over everything else.

"But I do not intend to let you leave so easily this ball which you have begun with him so imprudently, saying that the excellent Signor Gerolamo Cardano is occupied with public lectures in Pavia while I, his creature, invite you publicly to defend his honor. He has refused this opportunity, but I want to remain with what little honor I have. With this warning I make an end to the dance you have begun; I am prepared to lock all exits so that neither he nor you shall leave the ball.

"Thus I advise you again that, in case the said Signor Gerolamo Cardano does not intend to write to me, acknowledging wisely that he was wrong, then he has no reason for complaint against me, but only against himself due to the improper conduct he has shown toward his former great friend.

"You should at least make certain that he also signs your cartel in his own hand as your associate in this dispute. Then I shall gladly and with full heart accept the generous offer made to me by both of you, namely, to dispute with both of you together on geometry, arithmetic, and in all disciplines which depend on them, as for instance astronomy, music, cosmography, perspective, architecture, and other topics which you offered above in your cartel.

"However, I do not accept, nor do I have to accept, the condition which you interpose next, namely, in that part where you say that you agree to dispute not only on such authors who have written on these subjects in Greek, Latin, or in the vulgar tongue, but also on my new invention, mentioned in my book and delighting me so much, provided I on my side agree to dispute on yours.

"This I can refuse because no challenge can be based or largely based on conditions which are prejudicial to him who is being challenged. It has been established by all authorities who have written upon challenges that any propositions which involve disadvantages to the challenged remain entirely free at his option.

"But this astute condition of yours has made me laugh and laugh, because I realize that you have imagined that you could make me follow a certain path, so that in the dispute I would not be allowed to propose anything to you but from those authors who have written on this subject which has been stated or declared in my book (a ridiculous thought).

"You believed firmly that I would not notice such a detail. From this I recognize your stupidity and even in two ways. First, in believing that I should be so dumb as not to notice the naïveté and importance of your condition. Secondly, are you not aware, poor thing, that with this condition you have disclosed and manifested to me the vileness of your heart and how you fear to enter into this festival which, important enough, was begun by you?"

It is amply evident how anxious Tartaglia was to bring Cardano into the argument. Quite properly his quarrel was with the author of the *Ars Magna,* and an added incentive may have been that Cardano was rapidly rising in European fame and an engagement with such a prominent figure would in itself be a distinction, while Ferrari as yet was a relatively unknown youngster against whom not even a victory would increase Tartaglia's standing materially.

Tartaglia imagined that the conditions for the dispute were formulated in such a manner that they concealed a trap, compelling him to dispute with Ferrari on the *Ars Magna,* a great handicap indeed. He continued by specifying the various conditions for the dispute and concluded as follows:

"The amount of money which I intend to deposit and similarly the problems to be disputed I shall disclose to you after the arrival of your reply which I shall expect thirty days after this has been presented to you. When this reply comes I honestly expect to soak the heads of both of you in the most excellent manner and both at the same time, a thing which no barber in all Italy can do. If you should not make a reply within this time, I shall let the intelligent men of the world pass judgment upon your qualities. I reserve the right to proceed further if I should so desire."

In a second cartel, dated April 1, 1547, Ferrari returned to the moral question of keeping scientific knowledge secret.

"First of all let me remind you, so that you don't remain astonished and wondering where I have heard all your lies, as if by a revelation of Apollo, that I was present in the house when Cardano offered you hospitality and I attended your conversations, which delighted me greatly. It was then that Cardano obtained from you this bit of a discovery of yours about the cube and the cosa equal to a number, and this languishing little plant he recalled to life from near death by transplanting it in his book, explaining it clearly and learnedly, producing for it the greatest, the most fertile, and most suitable place for growth. And he proclaimed you the inventor and recalled that it was you who communicated it when requested.

"What more do you want? 'I don't want it divulged,' you say. And why? 'So that no one else shall enjoy my invention.' And therein, although it is a matter of small importance, almost of no utility, you show yourself un-Christian and malicious, almost worthy of being banned from human society. Really, since we are born not for ourselves only but for the benefit of our native land and the whole human race, and when you possess within yourself something good, why don't you want to let others share it? You say: 'I will publish it, but in my own book.' And who forbids it? Perhaps it is because you have not solved it entirely and therefore cannot compose as many volumes as you wish, and if it pleases you, discuss your invention still six hundred times.

"To this I add: does this seem to you to be a sufficiently good reason to attack with such impudence a man of intellect and highest knowledge who had praised you to the very learned envoy of the emperor and to his Excellency Alfonso d'Avalos? And now: I can prove as clear as daylight that not even we were ignorant of the fact that this was not your invention. If you do not permit Cardano to teach your discoveries to us, then at least you will permit him to instruct us in those of others."

Ferrari went on to tell about the visit to Bologna and how the secret was found to be included in the papers of del Ferro. To this Tartaglia retorted in a second countercartel.

"I must say in reply that I am very glad you were the person present in his house when I demonstrated my invention. But I wonder how you and he (for I know you speak only according to his mouth) can dare to reduce my invention in such a manner since you clearly had intended to immortalize yourself by it. Do you not perceive that every intelligent person is aware of this?

"He himself confessed that my invention was the soul of his book. Still he is not ashamed to say that all the other theorems found there are your inventions, except that of mine, about which he relates that I had rediscovered it five years before I showed it to him with many particulars, as for instance, the theorem about the census and the cube being equal to a number, and other similar ones, as is well known by many here in Venice. Furthermore, at that time I would not divulge it to his Excellency because he did not try to find the method, knowing that such a thing would be easy due to the vigor of my humble little plant.

"Concerning your statement that he published it under my name and mentioned me as inventor I shall reply that he did this in the belief that he could thus keep me quiet, but I have suffered greatly by the fact that he has broken his oath, an act which ought to make him red in the face from embarrassment."

The exchange of cartels and countercartels continued for a year and a half in 1547 and 1548. They are full of charges from both sides: Tartaglia repeatedly pointed out Cardano's "infamy" while Ferrari maintained that Tartaglia had not presented the events and the letters correctly. Tartaglia insisted on addressing the later cartels both to Cardano and to Ferrari and made every effort to bring in Cardano as a participant in the dispute, while Ferrari was equally insistent that the challenge had been issued by him personally and the controversy stood between him and Tartaglia and no one else.

Each side issued a series of thirty-one problems and the solutions submitted in return were criticized at great length. Tartaglia also continued to argue suspiciously on the details of the proposed dispute, on the rules for the disposition of the prize money, the choice of impartial referees, and the place for the encounter; after a while it becomes evident that he felt no inclination to accept the challenge and thus climax the quarrel in oral dispute. The first cartels appeared in rapid succession until Ferrari issued his fifth broadsheet in October 1547. For more than eight months no reply was received from Tartaglia and it appeared almost as if he had abandoned the whole controversy; then, suddenly he returned to the arena with a complete change of heart.

"Certainly you, Messer Gerolamo, and you, Messer Lodovico, have polished the boots so well for your own side that it reminds me of Astolfo of England who in his own words wanted himself to be the first horseman in the world, but when he jumped he always found himself showing his heels to the sun, and for this he always blamed his horse. Although this same thing has already happened to both of you in your arguments, nevertheless, to make this still clearer to the world, I shall presently make it happen to you again, because I intend to steer you along such a narrow path that you shall not be able to escape from my hands. Now to the facts. I make it understood to both of you that I merrily accept to join you in the real contest. Since destiny has brought me so near to you I shall not inconvenience you to go anywhere, neither to Rome, nor Florence, nor Pisa, nor Bologna, for I have decided to have the matter cleared up perfectly by coming personally to Milan."

Ferrari immediately returned to the fray with his sixth

and last cartel and informed his opponent that he was well aware of the reasons for his sudden willingness to accept the challenge. Through some noble patrons Tartaglia had been invited to return to Brescia to lecture on geometry, but the offer had probably been made on the condition that he establish his qualifications by concluding the much publicized dispute with Ferrari. Ferrari proceeded in vigorous language.

"I do not understand how you are led to the belief that I should behave like Astolfo, that is, first talk bravado and then turn my heels to the sun when I jump, because I have never participated in any dispute except with you and that well-known friend of yours [da Coi]. It appears to me that in these two disputes what happened was exactly the opposite of what you say. Your friend became so stupefied in the presence of the whole city and the most excellent judges appointed for the occasion that he showed his heels after his failure, and my appointment in Milan was confirmed. Until now I have treated you such that you have shown your heels to Venice, and although this time you have landed in the very honorable town of Brescia, I doubt strongly whether next time you will be able to jump from Brescia to a place worthy of a person as learned as you. I beg you, consider if all this indicates that I fall or whether I make others fall with their feet in the air when they jump."

Ferrari continued this sarcasm in another vein.

"The height of extravagance in your last reply is that this time you address yourself even to me and not only to another [Cardano] as you have done in all your other replies in this dispute. You say that I have written you letters and made promises under oath, of I don't know what, and finally that I have deceived you. I believe I see, Messer Niccolò, what you want to produce by these figments: you want to bring me to such a rage that I shall call you a bag of lies so that you may leave the letters aside and attack me bodily with arms. But in all faith I must try to avoid this because I have heard it said that you are such a beast of a man that I had better not fight you.

"But it should be enough to recall to your memory that you have never had any letters from me nor any promises except those I have made in my cartels. Although it is superfluous to demonstrate your obvious lies, nevertheless, I cannot desist from pointing out that you have already confessed to this by your own words, if you will reread your first and second ripostes. Here you repeat more than once that before my first challenge you had never had anything to do with me nor had you received any offense from me before the cartels, not even in these or in any other way.

"But you are really a devil of a man, wanting to be an inventor when you have the head of an adder which can understand nothing, everything going in one ear and out the other. I say this not to mock you, but rather in praise, because you are capable of wriggling like an eel so that one will lose you however strong a grip one may have. However, I believe that the past cartels have broken your backbone so thoroughly that there remains only a little wriggle of the tail. If there still is any vigor left, this is the time to show it because otherwise you will pass your future years immersed in the mud of ignominy, celebrated as the triumph of ignorance and malefaction.

"I see no other extravagances on which I should reply to you; you have written that Signor Gerolamo praises you in one of his works, but this does not concern me except insofar as you condemn yourself thereby. Signor Gerolamo has been able to attribute that result to its first inventor, namely, Scipione del Ferro of Bologna, and besides him also to Maria Fiore, who knew it before you as you confess in your book; nevertheless, he has been so courteous that he wanted to believe also that you had found it without having received it from either one of them or from any of their pupils.

An Elizabethan card party. This painting of Lord Burleigh playing primero has been ascribed to Zuccaro.

Gerolamo Cardano at the age of sixty-eight.

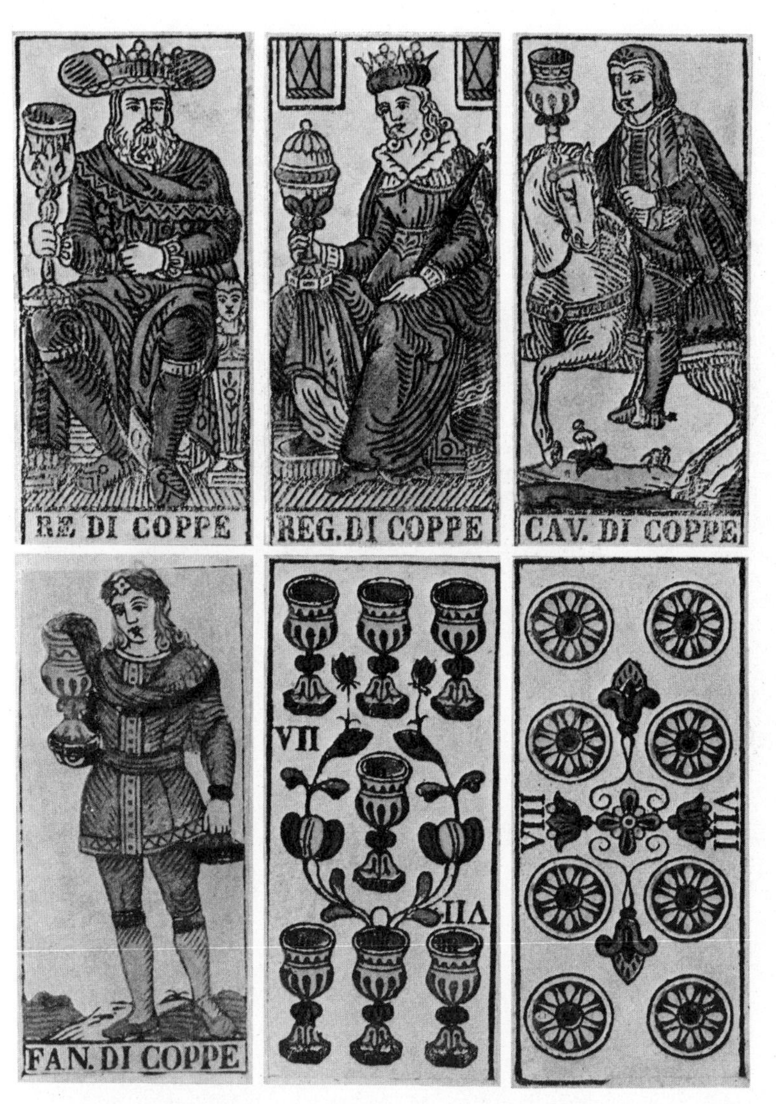

Playing cards, printed in Milan about the time of Cardano,
found in the wainscoting of a palace in Venice.
[Courtesy Mrs. Samuel H. Fisher Card Collection,
Yale University Library.]

A reproduction from the famous painting "The Cardsharps" by Caravaggio, 1593.

"He has praised you together with both of them and instead of accepting this benefit (as well as those which I have mentioned in my second cartel and many others to which I can testify) you have so indecorously and villainously written about him that it seems you must be out of your mind. But I rejoice that the virtue, humanity, and learning of his Excellency is so well known to the whole world that the ignominy of such a return falls back entirely upon you. Furthermore, even if some of these malignant and invidious remarks should reach judicious and august ears, he has occasion to be content to have been evilly spoken about by a man of your low level, because the wholehearted praise of the good and the blame which stems from the malicious envy of a culprit are worth the same and may be used for the same coin: and this has been said briefly to repulse your evil talk; should I leave my natural modesty behind and answer in a way which would be required with a person like you, I should have to make it known to the world that you are a man whose ability to compose false accusations can be compared to none."

It was a gala occasion in Milan when the dispute finally took place on August 10, 1548, in the Church in the Garden of the Frati Zoccolanti (the wooden-shod Franciscan brethren). High officers, nobles, and distinguished citizens were present and Don Ferrante di Gonzaga, the governor of Milan, had been named the supreme arbiter. The topic of the dispute was to be the problems which had been proposed in the cartels and the solutions which had been submitted.

It is unfortunate that we have no records of the proceedings from independent sources; the only accounts are certain brief statements which Tartaglia has inserted in his two subsequent books. However, he was personally too involved and can hardly be expected to give an entirely impartial description; furthermore, his various remarks seem to be somewhat at variance with one another.

The first short notices date from 1551, a few years after the encounter, and here Tartaglia made rather light of the whole matter; in a fictitious dialogue with his favorite pupil, the Englishman Richard Wentworth, he related that the dispute did not cause him much work and he enjoyed it greatly. A little later in the same book he said that he had nothing to do in Brescia that summer since all the students were away on harvest work, and so he decided, contrary to the advice of some of his friends, that he might as well journey to Milan to conclude the dispute, which had been held in abeyance after he had exchanged the cartels with Ferrari and Cardano.

Cardano had left town but Ferrari appeared with a great group of followers.

"But when the contest began I made them see and confess that they had erred not a little in the problem from the *Geography* of Ptolemy. But when I wanted to proceed to their other solutions, in order to disturb me, all those present did not want me to continue and requested loudly that I should also let him speak, and so it all remained confused. Then he began his declarations on the problem of Vitruvius which I had not solved, and he talked and talked on it; and subsequently also on the construction of a regular polygon with seven sides. I told him that he should give me his solutions in writing and with this statement the matter came to an end and I returned to Brescia."

Shortly before Tartaglia died his principal work appeared, the *Trattato Generale di Numeri et Misure,* printed in Venice in 1556. This is an excellent text, well composed and easy to read, but almost throughout it is of a most elementary nature. It begins at the very lowest level with the rules of counting, addition, subtraction, goes on to simple arithmetic and geometric problems, extraction of roots, some equations, and amusement problems. Numerous chapters are devoted to commercial calculations, the rule of three, and particularly the *cambia* or exchange between the many Italian towns and principalities. Much of the material is still interesting from a historical point of view, and as a textbook it was widely used.

In some sections, particularly the later ones, Tartaglia returns to the challenge problems of the cartels, giving his own solutions, deprecating those of his opponents, and displaying systematically in the margin, sometimes in several places on the same page, the warning to the reader, "Error or mistake committed by Cardano, physician, and Lodovico Ferrari, his creature." Some of these observations may be justified, but in some instances he picks on mere trivialities.

In the introductory epistle to the reader he explains that the work had been much delayed by various difficulties which he had encountered: "the most pleasant of these was caused by my friends in Milan who kept me entertained a whole year by writing manifestoes."

Later on when he begins to explain the challenge problems, he prefaces the discussion with an account of the dispute so that his criticisms can be better understood. He explains first that the dispute was really superfluous because he was already victorious through the fact that he had solved the problems proposed to him within a few days while the opponents had greatly exceeded the stipulated time limit.

"But since I was at that time in Brescia, to which city I had been prevailed upon to return—with great promises and meager returns—by certain learned doctors and noble Brescians for the purpose of lecturing publicly on Euclid's geometry, I decided finally, in order to make an end to these cartels which in the future will trouble humanity, to travel to Milan to expound personally and publicly how their solutions, as I said, to the greater part were entirely false. And so, to cut it short, I rode to Milan.

"With printed cartels I invited them both to appear

the following Friday, August 10, 1548, at 18 o'clock in the Church of the Garden of the Frati Zoccolanti, to dispute those criticisms which I intended to present against the solutions they had submitted to my thirty-one problems, seven months after the time limit.

"When Gerolamo Cardano was informed he immediately rode away from Milan to avoid being present at the dispute. Thus on the appointed day there appeared only Lodovico Ferrari with a great crowd of his gentleman friends and others, while I was alone except for my brother, who had accompanied me from Brescia.

"I presented myself before the crowd and explained briefly to them the reasons for our public dispute and the cause for my coming to Milan. But when I wanted to reprove their false solutions of my thirty-one questions, they began, in order to confuse me, to hold up the proceedings with talk and nonsense on the proposal that certain men who were present should be elected judges. But since they were his friends and unknown to me, I would not consent to such an astute maneuver but said that I wanted all those present to be judges together with all those to whom the criticisms would be sent after they had been printed.

"So finally they let me talk and in order not to fatigue the noble listeners with tiresome arguments about numbers and geometry I first turned to the solution given on the problem from the twenty-fourth chapter of Ptolemy's *Geography*, my own eighteenth question. And I compelled them to admit there that it could not be denied that it had been solved or concluded falsely by them.

"But when I wanted to proceed further almost all the spectators began to shout loudly that I should also let him speak on those solutions which I had found (in about three days only) of the thirty-one questions he had put to me. It availed me nothing to remonstrate and tell them to let me complete those criticisms which I had intended to make and let him, whom they wanted, speak afterward. But all my reasoning and complaints made no impression; they unanimously refused to let me proceed further and required that he should be permitted to express himself.

"He, therefore, began to speak and said that I had not known how to solve his fourth problem on Vitruvius, and we argued so long on his question that suppertime had come and everyone was compelled to leave the church and go home.

"It became clear to me that it was impossible for me to fulfill my intention of speaking convincingly to the whole multitude, and since I began to fear that worse was to come, I left next day without saying a word and returned to Brescia by another road. However, my intention was to make public in print all the things which I had not been permitted to complete orally.

"This I could have done a few months afterward, but then another major calamity occurred to me: when I expected to collect the stipend which I had been promised by the Brescian doctors and nobles for my public lectures, they sent me from Herod to Pilate so long that I was compelled to enter into a lawsuit against the person who had been commissioned to make the promise. My intention had been to bring the suit to a quick decision in a couple of weeks, but they were all such past masters in the art of litigation that they kept it going for eight months. Finally, the agent in whose name the offer was made was acquitted and I was advised to proceed against the principal among those who had led me to come. However, he was one of the foremost lawyers in Brescia and I did not have the courage to sue him.

"But adding it all up, the damages, the interest, the moving expenses for bringing my whole family to Brescia, the loss of almost all salary for the year and a half during which I lectured publicly, the expense of the law suit, moving expenses back to Venice, in addition to the many other peculiar disasters which fortune added, in this also a danger of plague in Brescia, all this made me lose my master quills and I was unable to execute what I had in mind to do."

This is only a very abbreviated account of Tartaglia's difficulties in Brescia; in the earlier work, *Terza Ragionamente* (1551), he devotes a large part of the book exclusively to a description of the dishonest dealings meted out to him in the town of his birth. The conditions for the invitation were disregarded; he was compelled to use up all his savings, and he enumerates at length all the wealthy patrons who had promised under oath to pay their subscription money but in the end broke their word.

All these happenings are presented in the form of a conversation with his faithful pupil Richard Wentworth, who commiserates deeply with him. The dialogue ends with a philosophical comment upon the nature of a man's word of honor:

"*Richard.* Dear friend, even if they have treated you so badly and for their sake you have suffered and lost so much, nevertheless, I perceive that you comfort yourself with the thought that they have actually lost much more than you, since, as Seneca says, a man who loses his honor has nothing else to lose.

"*Niccolò.* To them it appears that a promise is actually not a promise, unless it is executed with legal documents and by the hand of a notary.

"*Richard.* With this saying of yours there comes to my mind a passage from Ariosto on these matters; he expresses it in the form:

Faith should never be corrupted
Be it given by one or a thousand together,
Be it in the forest, or in a cave
Far from town or in the middle of the city.

It should hold as before a court, with a crowd
Of witnesses, with legal documents and records.
Without swearing oaths and other express signs,
It shall suffice that he has promised."

We have no record of the official verdict, but it is evident that Ferrari was declared the winner of the dispute while Tartaglia suffered an ignominious defeat. Tartaglia was a disputant of great experience and must have known full well that he forfeited all hope of victory by leaving the engagement before it was concluded. What actually happened is difficult to say, but it seems hard to believe that such an important contest, held under high auspices and before a distinguished audience, should have been permitted to deteriorate into a rowdy argument with the public. Tartaglia may have lost his temper; he may have been called to order; he evidently exceeded his time and monopolized the rostrum. Afterward it would have been quite natural to put the blame on his opponents to make the events appear in a more favorable light. Since Tartaglia's reports are the only ones available, some historians have accepted them at face value, but the justification for this seems very slim, particularly in view of the subsequent fate of the two opponents.

Tartaglia never mentioned any specific reason, except the vileness of his fellow men, why his salary was not paid in Brescia, but it is not at all unlikely that it was connected with his poor showing in Milan; afterward he returned to his modest position as abacist or teacher of mathematics in Venice.

For the winning side there was little cause for prolonged explanations of motives and actions. Cardano mentioned the affair only in passing in his biography of Ferrari, stating without further comment that he had a public dispute with da Coi and later another with Tartaglia, defeating them both. Ferrari's reputation was greatly enhanced by the victory; shortly afterward he received a host of flattering offers, among them calls to lecture in Rome and in Venice, Tartaglia's own city, as well as an invitation from the emperor to serve as tutor for his son.

Several writers have attempted to evaluate the relative merits of this trio of mathematicians, Cardano, Ferrari, and Tartaglia. Most seem to agree that, on the basis of their published works, leaving out all hypotheses about what they may have achieved otherwise, Cardano and Ferrari represent by far the greater mathematical penetration and wealth of novel ideas. Tartaglia was also, doubtless, an excellent mathematician, but his great tragedy was the head-on collision with the only two opponents in the world who could be ranked above him. Without them he would most likely have been reckoned as the foremost mathematician in the middle of the sixteenth century; in comparison with them, all his ideas take on an elementary aspect. Moritz Cantor, the dean of historians of mathematics, was even willing to state—again as far as Tartaglia's printed works are concerned—that, had Tartaglia never existed, the science of mathematics would not have been deprived of a single great or fertile idea.

This brings us to a rather peculiar circumstance in Tartaglia's scientific production: he talked repeatedly and wrote about the great work in algebra which he was preparing, yet nowhere, not even in the *Trattato*, his last and most extensive book where topics of this kind would have fitted in organically, did he discuss anything but elementary questions; nowhere are third degree equations discussed. His publisher related how, after Tartaglia's death in 1557, he took great care to gather all of the mathematician's posthumous papers from which the last volume of the *Trattato* was prepared; no trace of further notes of importance could be found.

Cantor indicated the possibility that Tartaglia himself may have obtained the solution of the cosa and the cube equation at second hand, and Ferrari also expressed some doubt as to its provenance. However, this seems to be going too far in detracting from Tartaglia's merits; there is not the slightest shred of evidence to show that he had not arrived at his cherished result through his own studies.

But on one point a deep injustice has persisted. Some of the early Italian algebraists referred to the formula for the solution of the cube and the cosa equal to a number proposition as "del Ferro's formula," but the influence of the *Ars Magna* was so great that it has forever since been known as "Cardano's formula." Cardano never made any claim to this invention. In present-day mathematical texts it should in no way be too late to begin to pay homage again to the original discoverer, del Ferro, and thus give credit where credit is due.

We have come to the end of our story about one of the first attempts to restrict the circulation of scientific information. Tartaglia had just cause for complaint that Cardano had broken a solemn pledge, but otherwise it cannot be maintained that he suffered a grave injustice; the facts were presented fairly and without hiding his share in the discovery.

Cardano, on the other hand, had made a promise whose consequences neither he nor anyone else could have foreseen at the time. Through it he had been driven into a position so extraordinary that it threatened his whole study and teaching of mathematics. In principle it is the same paradoxical situation which in the long run seems unavoidable if secrecy is practised in scientific studies. We know through experience that it may be justified in times of crises, for specific purposes, but if extended for more than short periods, it will in the end, surely and inexorably, lead to the most confusing, even absurd, situations.

Cardano the Gambler

According to his own numerous confessions Cardano gambled, for years even to excess, and almost all writers on his life, including Cardano himself, have dutifully expressed their most sincere condemnation of such an immoral and disreputable pastime. But in Cardano's younger years it was often not a matter of choice; whatever uncertain surplus he could gather by play was a most welcome addition to a less than meager income from his medical practice.

When medieval writers had occasion to refer to gambling, it was mostly for moralizing purposes. Games of chance were joined in an unholy trinity, chess, tables, and dice, and after the beginning of the fifteenth century cards were added to the list. In all of these Cardano was evidently an expert. Today, when life is under the impact of entertainment in all forms, it may perhaps be a little difficult to visualize the extent to which games dominated social life in medieval and Renaissance times. The study of ancient games is a fascinating topic, but when it comes to the question of exact details—how these games were actually played—we must confess that our information is quite scant. Names of classical and medieval games are preserved in abundance, many of their technical terms are even preserved in present-day expressions, but the writers who had occasion to mention the games played in their day usually assumed that the reader was entirely familiar with all details.

In Renaissance literature one finds extensive enumerations of popular games. Most famous among them is the long list of several hundred games with which Rabelais lets his giant Gargantua amuse himself in his youth; however, the majority of them are children's games, not games of chance. Cardano was obsessed with the spirit of compilation and systematization in all fields of human endeavor, so in his book on chance it is likely that he gathered the names of all the games he knew of or had heard about. On the whole the games he mentions are in good agreement with those one finds in other sixteenth-century works; for instance, many of them appear also in Rabelais' list.

Chess, the queen of games, is at present considered a purely intellectual pastime, but in the Middle Ages it was customary to play for money, and usually in a fast and furious manner. To even the chances of two unequal opponents it was played with handicaps of certain pieces according to their strength; the chess problems were also favorite betting propositions. Cardano was an excellent chess player, and according to his own statements he collected much material on the game. Perhaps his most reliable gambling income was derived in this manner. In his *Autobiography* he related the following little tale:

"It was in the summer of the year 1542 when I fell into the habit of going every day to the house of Antonio Vimercati, a noble in our town, for the purpose of playing chess. We played for stakes from one to two *reals* a game, and since I won constantly I could take home every single day about one gold piece, sometimes less, sometimes more. For him it must have been an onerous pleasure; for me it was both game and profit. But through this habit I had fallen so low, that for two years and some months I neglected my medical practice, my other incomes, my reputation, and my studies. One day toward the end of August, when my opponent may have tired of losing so regularly and understood that I had all the advantages, he decided to quit. In order that he should not be deflected from his purpose for any reason, by any regret or temptation, he forced me to swear that in the future I would never enter his house for the purpose of playing. I swore this by all gods, and so this day became the last at the game and I devoted myself entirely to my studies."

21. The various intellectual levels of games. From Petrarch, *Glück und Unglück* (1572).

The standard medieval gambling instruments were the dice, the invention of the devil according to all moralizing sermons. In Cardano's day the most common dice games were of the so-called hazard type; presumably they were of Arabic origin and came to Europe around the time of the Crusades; the name hazard itself is derived from *al zahr*, the Arabic term for the die. During the centuries these games have changed a good deal and numerous varieties have appeared, but some of the basic principles have persisted. The American crap game is a viable and exuberant direct descendant, a streamlined version of the ancient hazard.

Midway between the dice and chess stand those games, containing both the elements of skill and chance in Cardano's system, which were usually called tables in Old English. All are varieties of our present backgammon, the French tric-trac or tic-tac, named onomatopoetically for the rattling sound of the dice in the cup. These are among the most ancient games in the world, the offspring in direct line from the Persian game of *nerd* or *nard*, which antedates chess by unknown centuries. The Romans played a variation of it under the name of *duodecim scripta*, "the game of the twelve lines."

Cardano talks steadily about the game of *fritillus*, and this is at first a little confusing since there exists no medieval game commonly known by this name. However, by collecting the various bits of evidence from the contexts, there can be little doubt that he had the game of tables in mind. But in translating the name "tables" into the Latin "fritillus," he is evidently the victim of a serious misunderstanding. The fritillus or the *pyrgus* was the dice cup in ancient Greek and Roman gambling, while Cardano seemed to believe that the fritillus was the gaming board. Therefore Cardano becomes somewhat confused at one point in the last chapters of his book on games, where, according to his own admission, he borrows from an earlier treatise by Calcagnini.

Calcagnini, in his description of classical games, used the terms correctly: *tessera* for the dice, *fritillus* for the cup, and *alveolus* for the gaming board. Cardano passes over the difficulty in the following words: "The game of tesserae is modified so as to be played with the fritillus (for that is not the pyrgus, but a gaming board, but you may take it so, I do not contend about words); then you would say that with the board (if that is acceptable) the game is very similar to human life."

Cardano lists a great number of varieties of backgammon, which probably differed only a little in the rules for moves or in the initial or final positions: *sperainum, speraia, speraionum* (also called *sbaraia*), *sbaraiaonum, sbarainum,* and the greater or lesser *tocadiglium.* He mentions the *Canis Martius,* "which requires an outstanding intelligence"; in contrast he notes "that the sbaraionum is the game of princes, and does not require thought."

Most of the medieval forms of tables were played with three dice, but in Cardano's time the two-dice varieties had become more popular, and a little later the three-dice games disappeared entirely; there was also an intermediate form which was nominally played with three dice, but one was taken to be fixed and assumed always to show a six. In his studies of the frequencies of the various throws in fritillus Cardano computes the figures both under the assumption of using two and three dice.

Chess, tables, and dice should seem to suffice both for Cardano's recreation and gambling, but there is every indication that card games fascinated him to at least the same degree. At the time when Cardano was rector of the University of Padua and began his gambling studies in earnest, playing cards were only a little more than a century old in Europe. But the variety of card games was already overwhelming; as Cardano said, "If I should speak of them all it would be an endless task." He mentioned such games as *primero, trappola, bassette, fluxus* (flush), *taro, tarochi, ulcus, triumph* (trumps) and *triumphetti, sanctius, cricones, one hundred, romfa,* and *scaltara.* Almost all of these were standard games which were played all over Europe; some of them still enjoy a healthy and popular life in nearly the same form. Trappola is reputed to be the oldest card game in Europe, and Cardano's few remarks about it are practically the only sources we possess, except that in Cardano's time it was transformed into *tarok,* which is still played in certain parts of Germany and Austria.

Primero was Cardano's favorite card game, and this favorite he shared with all of Europe in the sixteenth century. He devotes more space to primero than to all other card games combined, and it is the only one for which he computes any chances. Primero must have been among the earliest card games in Europe, and from it one can follow a fairly-well-defined lineage directly to our present-day popular pastime, a fast and furious poker game. It is true that the bids in primero were somewhat different and the hands consisted of only four cards, but the spirit seems to have remained much the same.

In England the game of primero had a hectic bloom in Elizabethan times. Shakespeare mentions it in *The Merry Wives of Windsor* where Falstaff complains, "I never prospered since I foreswore myself at primero." In *Henry VIII* the king plays primero with the Duke of Suffolk, and in several other plays one finds allusions to the terms of the game. But in spite of its popularity and the numerous references to the game in Elizabethan literature there does not seem to remain a single English source which explains the rules of primero; several of Shakespeare's commentaries pass over the term with the superficial observation that it was the name of a difficult card game.

On the Continent the game remained in popular favor much longer than in England. In France the rage of *prime* reached its pinnacle in the beginning of the seventeenth century when it was played everywhere, in the royal salons as well as in the taverns and the soldiers' camps; even such serious-minded statesmen as the cardinals Mazarin and Richelieu devoted much time and money to it. Toward the end of the seventeenth century primero became obsolete, and it was superseded by the still more hazardous banking game of *bassette*, "the game of desperate men" as Cardano characterized it.

The European homeland of primero was probably Italy, where it has flourished for nearly five centuries. As early as 1500 it was looked upon as an ancient game, and as late as the nineteenth century it was among the most common card games; it is still not an extinct game, although the present Italian version is considerably simpler than its Renaissance ancestor. It was then a lively and varied game, primarily perhaps a game of chance, but it was intermingled with liberal opportunities for personal enterprise and skill, for daring in bidding and bluffing, for cunning in discards and draws, all entirely in accordance with the exuberant spirit of the period. Thus it is not surprising to find that primero was a beloved vehicle for Italian poets as an allegory on the vicissitudes of life in the sixteenth century.

"The primero is such a wonderful game," says the imaginary Messer Pietropaulo de San Chirico in his poem on the game, and after having created both his brainchild and his poetic eulogy of primero the writer, Francesco Berni (1497-1536), supports them with a burst of enthusiasm in his detailed commentary, "Where is the emperor, the king, the prince, who does not play at primero and thereby does not become more generous and brave? Perhaps without this he would not succeed in being so. Is there a citizen, an artisan, a farmer or a man so poor and solitary that he does not pursue this game like the crazy woman her son?"

Shortly afterward Berni pays another compliment to his patrons, the nobles, and continues in his praise of the game: "I said above that the noblemen become more liberal and generous through primero; although this is true it may perhaps be a little difficult to believe, since generosity is a natural virtue of the nobles. But what shall one say when one finds a miser, a lazy and vile man, a poor devil, who by playing primero becomes generous, splendid, brave, and rich and as a consequence, famous and praised to the sky by everyone. A man who is not a good fellow, in one word, not a gentleman, should not play this game since it involves nothing staining the purity of one's soul. It embraces the three principal virtues, faith, hope and charity, and these accompanied by patience, modesty, longanimity, prudence, kindness, and charm, indeed, by all cardinal and theological virtues."

This composition of Berni, *Capitolo del Gioco della Primiera,* was completed in 1526 and is an excellent specimen of the original *poesia bernesca* in which the author exuberantly burlesques serious topics and solemnizes frivolous matters. Here Berni analyzes word for word a poem about primero, evidently written by himself, parodying the gravity and pedantry of the best sellers in reading in Italy in his day, the Dante commentaries. The *Capitolo* appeared just at the time when Cardano was gathering his first notes on the subject of games and it is quite likely that it is this book to which Cardano refers obliquely in chapter five of the *Ludo Aleae* when he explains why he has dealt with gambling. Cardano seems to have been lacking in a sense of humor and he often seems inclined to take statements in a too literal meaning. No wonder, therefore, that Berni's levity did not appeal to him: "Thus it is not absurd for me to discuss gambling, not in order to praise it—for I have known some writers to attempt this, but their efforts are vain and form a bad example."

Most sources give but a meager description of the Renaissance primero. Indeed, Cardano's account of the bids is the most detailed information we possess. The game was played with a deck of forty cards, with the eight, nine, and ten spots removed. Each hand of four cards could produce a series of bids. The two lowest were the *numerus* or point bids, consisting either of two or three cards in the same suit, in other words, a two or three card flush in our modern terminology.

The main bid, the *primero,* came next, and here all four cards had to belong to different suits. Then followed a very special bid, the *supreme point,* a three card flush containing the six, seven, and ace in the same suit; these were the three cards of the highest point value. The highest bid was often the *fluxus* or flush with all four cards in the same suit, but in some versions this could be beaten by the *chorus* or four of a kind, that is, the primero with four cards of the same denomination, like four kings or four sixes. A further difference from the present poker was produced by the point values of the individual cards, so that each bid would also have a point sum; when several players had the same type of bid this became the deciding factor. Cardano lists the various values and analyzes at great length the smallest and highest sums which can appear in each case.

As to the rules of play, let us emphasize that there can be no question of laying them down in a hard and fast way. Just as poker has varied from time to time, from country to country, so also the game of primero had many versions. Even as early as in Cardano's youth it was pointed out by Berni that practically every city in Italy had its own rules; personally he favored the rules in use at the court in Rome because, as he observed, they were more liberal than elsewhere.

When the game began each player deposited the stakes and received two cards. These could be exchanged once or even several times until someone had received two cards which seemed so promising to him that he was willing to announce a *vada* ("it goes") and open the bidding. The other players could remain in or drop out according to their wishes, but if no one else was willing to participate, the last man after the opener was obliged to continue.

The *rest,* or next two cards, was then distributed; this term was also commonly applied to the amount which one was permitted to stake on the completed hand. This concluding bet was usually restricted by advance agreement in order to keep the gambling within reasonable bounds. Thus the expression "to set one's rest" was originally synonymous with "doing one's utmost," but in England it acquired a double entendre which is readily perceptible, for instance, from the contexts of the jocular passages in Shakespeare where the expression is introduced.

In the final round of betting a player with a primero or a four card flush was obliged to announce the type of bid in his hand. Thus the opponents would to some extent be aware of their chances. On the other side, the players with lower bids had the privilege of discarding and drawing one or two cards before the game was decided by the showdown.

At this stage of the game there entered a custom which evidently was in widespread use. Quite often there would be only two players left toward the end, one with a high bid and the other with a lower bid, but with some chances of conquering his adversary through a fortunate draw. The last player could then offer an agreement, a *fare a salvare,* to salvage some of his stakes, on the principle that the accumulated pot should be divided in proportions corresponding somewhat to the respective chances of the two opponents. It is for this purpose, as we shall see, that Cardano makes his probability studies for obtaining a primero or a flush and, incidentally, discovered that the customary divisions usually favored the underdog.

Let us not keep concealed that the fare a salvare by many was not considered a quite honorable and courageous procedure, and several writers condemn this kind of pusillanimous arrangement. In their opinion the knights of the primero should rather fight to the bitter end, taking their chances as fate decreed. Pietro Aretino compares them to cowardly soldiers who run away when the battle looms, to poltroonly mercenaries only concerned about finding a safe spot where the booty might be divided. Berni, on the other hand, is more tolerant and finds that it must be excused in certain emergencies, "for," as he put it, "it must be admitted that sometimes a person for fear of losing all he possesses in this world is compelled to do something which is below the standards of decorum for a well-bred man." He finds also that history shows many a good precedent for such action. "One must honestly try to remedy the situation in the best possible way, just as princes do in war. In order to defend their own states they run away from one friendship into another without regard to honesty or shame and they measure their friends and foes only according to the profits which they believe they can derive from them."

It must be conceded that we have given but a pale and inadequate picture of the actual primero scene with its lively actions and innumerable special conventions, the bonus for the bids, false declarations, transfer of hands, sidebets, and coalitions among the players. A good primero game was as varied and unpredictable as Italian politics, according to the authors.

Italy had not enjoyed many peaceful periods during the Renaissance, but in Cardano's lifetime the turmoil of war became so intense that even the Italians were horrified. The contending ruling families of the small Italian principalities were ever-ready for strange maneuvers and sinister coalitions. Any chance of gaining power, money, or prestige was always worth the risk of war.

The Holy See had its own ambitious schemes for wordly aggrandizement which led the popes to play a cunning but often unwise political game. But the dominant forces, which at any time could bring the tension to a snapping point, came from the outside. Two lifelong rivals made Italy the principal arena for their contest: Francis I, King of France, and Charles V, King of Spain and ruler of the Holy Roman Empire, titular overlord of the German states. The French poet Mellin de Saint-Gelais (1491-1558) describes the political intrigues in Italy, the game among the pope, the king, and the emperor in terms which needed no explanation for his contemporaries:

The king, the pope, the German ruler
Play a jolly game of primero.
The weapons are their vada, the invite is Italy.
The king has the supreme point in his hand—
The Roman pastor has fifty-one;
He is tormented and melancholy.
With paled face the emperor waits;
He hopes to collect money for his bid.
The pope proposes an agreement.
The emperor ponders, hardly daring to glance at his cards;
He fears they will show clubs or swords [spades].
The king advises him: don't expect any gain;
This is my game, here is the supreme point
Which takes the money in the pot.
Alas, whoever may be victor
The loss falls on the Holy Father.
The emperor is torn between fear and hope,
Disclosing cagily his cards only little by little,
For in this game skill is worth less than luck.

Cardano's own life was greatly influenced by the raging wars; as a child he had watched the marching Spanish soldiers from his mother's house in Milan. His studies at the University of Pavia were interrupted by the campaigns of the French and Spanish armies which culminated in the ignominious defeat of Francis in the battle of Pavia in 1525. While the French king languished in Spanish captivity the German and Spanish mercenaries enjoyed their supremacy, and their celebration culminated in the gruesome sack of Rome in 1527, where the horrors so exceeded customary warfare that all of Italy was dazed and shaken.

Cardano, like most Italians, tried to play a fare a salvare in this turmoil; the fighting was left mainly to the professional soldiers and the citizens tried to preserve life and property by not antagonizing the prevailing powers. Cardano does not seem to have taken any stand and he was favored with generous offers from all sides—the king, the pope, and the emperor; all vied for his services as court physician. When the Spanish finally dominated Milan he was evidently satisfied to please the emperor and records proudly that he marched in a place of distinction near the baldachin in the procession in honor of Charles V's arrival in Milan. He made a suggestion for the emperor's comfort by designing an undercarriage for the emperor's vehicle so that he could travel at greater ease over the rough roads of the empire. This was the ingenious suspension device which still bears Cardano's name; at present one of its main uses is in compass suspensions at sea, but in principle it is also the idea applied in the universal joint of our automobiles, which in several European countries is still called a "cardan."

Cardano's book on gambling, *Liber de Ludo Aleae*, did not appear in print until it was rescued from the pile of his posthumous manuscripts and included in his complete works when they appeared in 1663. Cardano mentions the book in several instances and it is evident from his remarks that what we have preserved is only a minor part of a much more ambitious undertaking. The *Autobiography* mentions two books only on games, but in discussing his writings elsewhere he is much more specific about the content and the scope of his plans.

"I was made rector of the university [in Padua] the following year and without cessation I gave myself up to my passion [gambling]. According to my custom I used the following procedure. First I collected a hodge-podge of facts about games and then this was later expanded into four books. The first of these was actually completed and dealt with the game of chess; it contained one hundred pages.

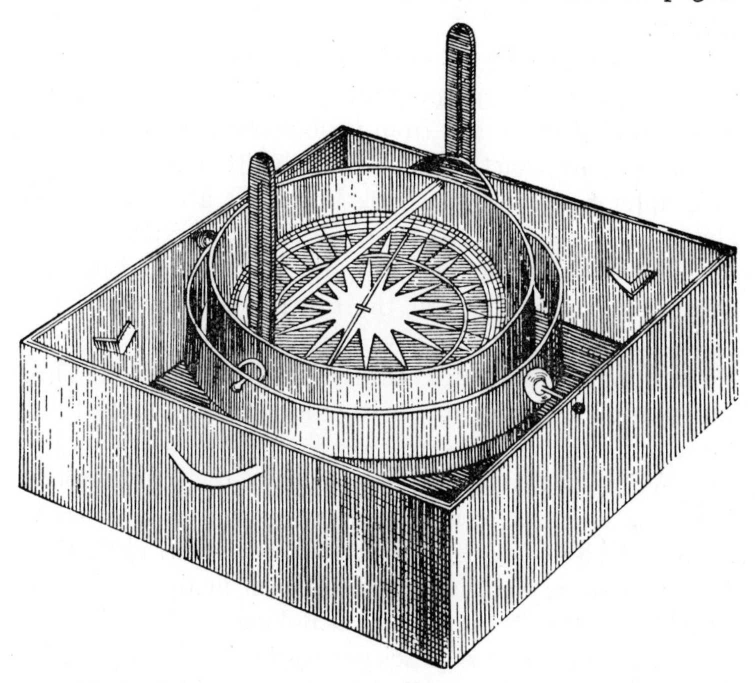

22. Cardano's suspension for a compass. From Bowditch, *Navigation*.

There are certain pages similar to this in the Basel edition of *De Subtilitate*. My book began 'not through any tricks,' for it was written in my native tongue [Italian]. The second book was on games which depend entirely on chance, as dice and primero. The section devoted to this took up twenty pages. The third was about games which depend both on luck and slyness as trappola and triumph. The fourth dealt with games combining luck and skill such as fritillus and many others."

From this it is clear that the large and complete section on chess is lost; possibly it was destroyed in the mass of manuscripts which Cardano burned before his death. The sections on dice and primero must be those which are included in this book and it also deals with trappola and fritillus.

The printed version of *De Ludo Aleae* must be a revised version of the original composition which Cardano began in his student years, and from various observations we can determine fairly exactly when it was rewritten. For instance, in chapter twenty of the book he relates a curious story about his gambling in the house of Thomas Lezius in Venice. He mentions that this was in the year 1526 and he was twenty-five years of age at the time; a little later he explains that he had difficulty in remembering the details since it happened nearly thirty-eight years before. This should make Cardano about sixty-four years old at the time the story was written, a few years after the death of his son. We know that Cardano spent some tragic and brooding years in Pavia revising and completing earlier manuscripts which he had laid aside, and so it seems likely that *De Ludo Aleae* was given its final form in this period or possibly shortly after his arrival in Bologna.

In many of his popular science works, in his moral writings, and even in his medical treatises Cardano expounds on the role of gambling in life, its pleasures and vices, its merits and demerits. In *De Utilitate* he warns against the acts which are most likely to bring a man to bankruptcy:

"Among these there are five: gambling, alchemy, architecture [presumably expensive building], lawsuits, and luxury. Gambling brings loss in two ways, first because a man loses money, secondly because he is led to neglect his business, arts, and studies. However, not all gamblers lose, but especially those who are either unskilled or unlucky or those who play with cheats."

In Cardano's remedies against melancholy gambling also

takes a part along with amulets, decoctions from certain plants, the drinking of ambrosia and light wine, sweet music, and association with girls and women "of the prudent sort." Among his other observations is the following: "It is helpful to think of the misery of those who were the cause of your melancholy."

Cardano mentions in several places the alleviation of his troubles through gambling when he was sick and melancholy. "But I do not believe that gambling is suitable for a man of sound mind except for the purpose of lightening cares which he would not otherwise be able to endure. Therefore, I think Augustus was unjustly criticized when, after he had twice been defeated by Sextus Pompeius in naval battles, he still continued to gamble. That he only played to lighten his mind is shown by the fact that when he was in perfect safety he always played without avarice or extravagance. Thus I would not condemn the princes who keep clowns, actors, and storytellers for the sake of relieving the anxiety which weighs heavily upon them, however, with this provision, that these creatures are used and not abused, that they possess them but are not possessed by them."

In Cardano's writings on how to win friends and influence people he advises: "One may please a man not only in a single way but in accordance with his whole nature and various feelings and habits. We assumed that he was a good man and therefore we must try to please him by virtuous actions, furthermore, by wise conversation, by stories and narrations, and by civic activities, but then also by jests and hunting. Moreover, gambling produces kindly feelings, perhaps rather more sometimes than is necessary. For friendship it is not so suited since it contains an element of the mean and sordid. Dice playing for much money is not suited for one or the other purpose, except in the case of princes."

He proceeds to give examples from Cicero on how gambling may produce peculiar acquaintances and how rulers in antiquity had gone so far as to appoint to judgeships fellow gamesters who had won their intimacy and good graces. "However, among private gentlemen that kind of association may be less advantageous since, if you have won much money, you may gain hatred, and if you lose, you may gain contempt. I pass by the fact that it is unbecoming and far from honorable. However, play without money is compatible with friendship, but it cannot produce friends, only kindly feelings." Dice, chess, and table games are not so beneficial, he considers, because these games are too competitive. He concludes by pointing out the ideal method: "To drink and eat together in general is a well trodden road to intimacy and good feelings and even friendship."

In the third chapter of *De Ludo Aleae* Cardano expresses the opinion that lawyers and doctors gamble at a disadvantage: if they win they may be called gamblers; if they lose they incur the risk that people may think them no better in their profession than at play. They may run into the same adverse criticism if they devote themselves too assiduously to music.

This, indeed, is a strange statement when one recalls that music was Cardano's chief recreation while gambling was an obsession with him. However, this is the kind of contradiction which can be found in abundance in Cardano's writings and which do not seem to concern him greatly. His books are cornucopias of good advice but they rather apply to others than to himself.

It is impossible to enumerate all the places in which Cardano tells of his gambling experiences. In *De Propria Vita* he also touches upon this topic in several places. In the chapter on his "Habits, Vices, and Errors" he expresses his feelings as follows:

"From my youth I was immeasurably given to table games; through them I made the acquaintance of Francisco

Sforza, Duke of Milan, and many friends among the nobles. But through the long years I devoted to them, nearly forty, it is not easy to tell how many of my possessions I have lost without compensation. But the dice treated me even worse, because I instructed my sons in the game and opened my house to gamblers. For this I have only feeble excuse: poor birth and the fact that I was not inept at the game."

He also devotes an entire chapter to "Gambling and Dicing":

"In perhaps no respect can I be deemed worthy of praise, but whatever this praise may be, it is certainly less than the blame I deserve for my immoderate devotion to table games and dice. During many years—for more than forty years at the chess boards and twenty-five years of gambling —I have played not off and on but, as I am ashamed to say, every day. Thereby I have lost esteem, my wordly goods, and my time. There is no corner of refuge for my defense, except if someone wishes to speak for me, it should be said that I did not love the game but abhorred the circumstances which made me play: lies, injustices and poverty, the insolence of some, the confusion in my life, the contempt, my sickly constitution and unmerited idleness, the latter caused by others. An indication of this is the fact that as soon as I was permitted to live a dignified life, I abandoned it all. It was not love for the game, nor a taste for luxury, but the odium of my position which drove me and made me seek its refuge. There are many remarkable discoveries in my book on games; there are several, eight or ten, which I have been unable to rediscover and seem to exceed human ingenuity. I leave these words to inform diligent and curious souls—I trust they will come—so that they may add this crown or pinnacle."

It is true that Cardano at times was in great need of supplementing his income by play, but it is equally true that he was intensely devoted to gambling even when his financial circumstances did not compel him to court the goddesses of luck. Twice he mentions the forty years during which he played at chess before he finally gave it up. Since he already played in his student days, it is interesting to note again that this corresponds roughly to the time when his son was executed and Cardano moved to Bologna.

De Ludo Aleae must be classified as a gambler's handbook, giving warning and advice to those with lesser experience than the veteran author. The book deals with false dice and marked cards and all the shady practices of gamblers. As a distinguished citizen Cardano might be criticized for discussing such questionable topics, including even his probability counts and his advice on the best methods to be used in play at dice. One has a feeling that Cardano closely safeguards his reputation and counterbalances possible objections by a very moral tone and attitude toward gambling. In some places his presentation is almost apologetic: "Even if gambling were altogether an evil, still, on account of the very large number of people who play, it would seem to be a natural evil. For that very reason it ought to be discussed by a medical doctor like one of the incurable diseases; for in every evil there is a least evil, in every disgrace a least disgrace, in every infamy a least infamy, and similarly in loss of time and fortune. Also, it has been the custom of philosophers to deal with the vices in order that advantage might be drawn from them, as for example in the case of anger. Thus it is not absurd for me to discuss gambling, not in order to praise it but in order to point out the advantages in it, and, of course, also its disadvantages, in order that they may be reduced to a minimum."

Cardano explains that play may be beneficial in times of grief and that the law permitted it to the sick and to those in prison and condemned to death. "In my own case when I thought after a long illness that death was close at hand, I found no little solace in playing constantly at dice. However, there must be moderation in the amount of money involved, otherwise, it is certain that no one should play."

This admonition that one should play only for small stakes is a recurrent theme in *De Ludo Aleae.* If one plays for high stakes, the game no longer gives relaxation but becomes a rack and torturer of the mind. Cardano repeats the view which is so often expressed in medieval moralizations on gaming that the loss to the loser is much greater than the gain to the winner, who will readily waste his easily acquired wealth. He rebukes the princes who played for high stakes to the detriment of their subjects and particularly the cardinal, who played with the Duke of Milan for five thousand crowns. "The greatest advantage in gambling comes from not playing at all," he says in one place, and similarly in another: "Certainly, in view of the small amount of pleasure which gambling provides and the rarity with which it favors our wishes, there are so many difficulties in it, and so many possibilities of loss, that there is really nothing better than not to play at all."

One of the very few places where *De Ludo Aleae* has been discussed even briefly is in Henry Morley's *The Life of Girolamo Cardano of Milan, Physician,* which appeared in 1854. However, it is difficult to reconcile the statements made by Morley with the actual content of Cardano's book: "The book is, at the same time, very characteristic of the writer's temper. Gambler himself and writing in that avowed character a treatise on his favourite amusement, Jerome takes no pains to defend his reputation or to justify a love of dice. He lays it down, coolly and philosophically as one of his first axioms that dice and cards ought to be played for money since if there be no stake to win there is nothing to mitigate the fact that time has been lost. To play at dice and cards for amusement purely, he says, when there are books, music, conversation, and so many wiser and better ways of passing time agreeably, is the part only of an empty man."

This interpretation can only be explained as an incorrect translation of Cardano's own words; the situation is exactly the contrary, namely, Cardano takes every precaution in his formulations to protect his reputation. Such misinterpretations, unfortunately, have a tendency to be preserved, and Morley's opinions have been reiterated elsewhere. The only passage which may be taken as a recommendation for high gambling, when quoted out of context, can be found in chapter eight. Here Cardano warns against playing even for small stakes in such a manner that one loses foolishly by not paying much attention to what is going on. This can only be permitted if one plays for nominal stakes or with his loved ones a short time after dinner. "But if you are determined to play for large stakes, then play constantly with an opponent who is neither more experienced than yourself nor more fortunate, and let the conditions not be unlucky for you."

While Cardano's literary or official attitude toward gambling is irreproachable, there is no doubt that his own behavior as a gamester suffered from exactly the faults he warns against. He emphasizes the anger provoked by losses in play as well as the concomitant quarrels and blasphemies, again fairly standard themes in the medieval descriptions of gamblers and dice games. But he most certainly also describes his own feelings on many occasions when the game had not gone his way: "The losses incurred include lessening of reputation, especially if one has formerly enjoyed any considerable prestige; to this is added loss of time, vain words, including on occasion curses against the gods, the neglect of one's own business, the danger that it may become a settled habit, the time spent in planning after the game how one may recuperate, and in remembering how badly one has played; there are also disputes and often, worst of all, provocation to anger; for then a man is carried away into playing for high stakes and into a feeling of enmity, so that he no longer has control of his own mind.

As a result, he throws out large sums of money and rather abandons them than plays for them. Play is a very good test of a man's patience or impatience. The greatest advantage in gambling comes from not playing at all. But there is very great utility in it as a test of patience; for a good man will refrain from anger even at the moment of rising from the game in defeat."

This was precisely one of Cardano's great defects; he was quick tempered and vindictive and often unable to control his anger. At times this involved him in brawls of the most serious kind. In chapter twenty of *De Ludo Aleae* Cardano tells, as we mentioned before, about a gambling session in Venice in the house of Thomas Lezius. Cardano made Lezius' acquaintance while he lived in Sacco and he refers to him as a senator and a patrician. At this time there must also have been weak sisters in this profession since his influence on Cardano seems to have been quite sinister and he charges him several times with using marked and soaped cards.

The story is interrupted abruptly in the text of *De Ludo Aleae* but the continuation can be found in his *Autobiography*:

"One time when I was in Venice on the birthday of the Holy Virgin [September 8, 1526] I had lost my money in gambling. The next day I lost what I had left in the house of the cheat. When I discovered that the cards were marked I drew my dagger and wounded him in the face, although only slightly. There were two young servants present and they had their spears stuck in the ceiling and the door was locked. I had grabbed all the money, both his as well as my own, my clothes and rings which I had lost to him the day before, but which I had by now regained and in part already sent back to my house with my servant. When I saw that I had wounded him I threw back some of the money and then attacked his servants. Since they were not skilled in using arms they begged me to spare their lives and I let them off on condition that they open the door. The commotion and confusion scared the master, who, as I suspect, had attracted me to his house only for false play, and feeling that the money now was of minor importance, he ordered them to open the door and I left.

"Since I had wounded a senator I tried to avoid the police, but at eight o'clock in the evening when I wandered around in the dark with the weapon under my cloak, I slipped and plunged into the sea. Fortunately I kept my head and with my right hand I grabbed the side of a passing boat and was saved by the passengers. I climbed on board, and to my surprise, there was the man with whom I had played. His face was bandaged to cover the wound, but he immediately offered me clothing from one of the sailors. I put them on and traveled all the way to Padua in his company."

The incident evidently left an indelible impression in Cardano's memory for he relates the incident in other works. In a discussion of his horoscope it becomes one of the critical points in his life:

"When I was twenty-five, during the eighth day of September (it was, however, toward the end of the year) I played and lost considerable money; on the following day I wounded a Venetian patrician, although I was in his house with his son and two servants and the doors of the house were locked. While they wished to avenge their master, they were not able to pull out their spears quickly enough and so after having opened the gates they sent me away fearfully, something I had not dared hope for. I feared the authorities, but at the second hour of the night, when I wanted to climb from a dingy to a ship, I fell into the sea. I had a heavy leather buffcoat on, and besides I did not know how to swim, but contrary to all hope, I was saved by grabbing a crossbeam and was hoisted on board by the sailors."

Most of the remaining discussion on the horoscope is

devoted to alleged connections between the planets and Cardano's various diseases.

Cardano intimates that gaming is a good way to make friends, and thus he had been introduced to many of the nobles of Milan; those of Venice he does not mention in this connection. In discussing the desirable characteristics of the players he points out the kind of game he liked and how an unpleasant opponent could spoil all pleasure from it, "for as a little bile in a great deal of honey and a little bit of rottenness in a large mixture of pleasant things can do far more to produce vomiting than all the rest can do to produce delight, so a blameworthy opponent, like a brandished sling, can drive far away all the pleasure of the game and all the peculiar delights derived from it." Some players "with many words disturb both themselves and others," some swear, some are contentious, "finally there are those who crack jokes to their adversaries; others are silent, which would be for the best if they did not demand the same from their opponents; there is a golden mean in everything." Cardano himself was undoubtedly of the talkative and rather easily excitable type who liked to express himself during the game: "That taciturnity which verges on utter silence is too hard and severe, since it is a greater pleasure to talk without playing than to play without talking."

Cardano's repeated warnings against playing with professional gamblers are again well-meant recommendations which he in no way followed himself. He advocates play only with adversaries of suitable station in life and upon appropriate occasions; Cardano enjoyed a game of this kind, but he probably never refused to gamble under any circumstances.

His knowledge of the tricks of the trade is extensive. Many medieval sources describe deceptions practiced by sharpers, but nowhere before Cardano does one find such a wealth of observations. He indicates only briefly the defects of the mispointed dice (the fullams in Shakespeare) and how the false dice may be tested, but without the detailed description which one finds in so many sources a century later, particularly in English gambling works. He does mention (in chapter thirty), however, some of the simplest trick throws with the dice: to "ride the dice," to "change the dice," and probably what is presently known as the "whip shot"; he also indicates the necessity of knowing the relative positions of the faces on the die when one wants to produce a particular point.

Cheating at cards seems to have interested Cardano more, and he enumerates a number of ways of marking them, all still in use today but considered to be rather old-fashioned to those more skilled in this still flourishing art. He mentions soaping of the cards to assist the dealer to deal from the bottom of the deck or to cut at suitable cards. Mirrors in rings to give the dealer a peep at the cards was already then old-fashioned; the *organum* or organ which he mentions is a device no longer in use; it seems to have been a slightly loose floor board which a bystander or player could move with his foot or by pulling a string to signal to his partner.

Curiously enough Cardano wonders why prestidigitators are not lucky in cards, since they should be able to use their legerdemain. The only explanation must be that Cardano never faced one as an adversary. He certainly was seriously impressed with their tricks according to his own confessions. When the Emperor Charles V made his triumphal entry into Milan in 1541, Cardano was the rector of the College of Medicine and as such was assigned the honor of serving as one of the carriers of the imperial baldachin. The emperor evidently knew the importance of catching the imagination of the populace, according to Cardano's description:

"I remember that when the Most Blessed Emperor Charles V came to Milan, during the dukeship of Francesco

Sforza, the second of that name, there was a Spaniard in his retinue by the name of Damautus, or Dalmagus, who did such wonderful things and so cleverly deceived the eyes of observers that those who knew something of philosophy considered him a magician. Neither in our times nor, as far as I know, in much earlier times has one ever seen his like, since he did many unheard-of and incredible things.

"Recently I made the acquaintance of Francesco Soma of Naples, a young man of high birth who by common account had scarcely reached his twenty-second year, and who, in addition to such exceptional skill in music that he has no equal in playing the lute, knows many incredible tricks of legerdemain. Among others there is one which I often witnessed together with my friends, and for which I have never been able to find a natural explanation.

"He spread the cards on the table, but in such a way that the pack was not separated, and then he asked us to take one card and conceal it. Then he took the pack, shuffled it, and guessed what card it was. This might perhaps have been attributed to quickness of hand; but that is by no means the case with what he did next. For when the card was put back in the pack and it was laid on the table, he asked several of us to draw a card, and we realized that the man who had drawn the card on the earlier occasion always drew the same card now, as though Soma were compelling us to draw the same card, or else were changing the face of the card.

"When I brought a clever man, an Epicurean philosopher, to the spectacle, he confessed that he could not discover how it was done, although he did not for that reason think we ought to admit that there is any power in these sublunary things beyond that which we see granted to them by nature. Thus this man evaded all our watchful care and surpassed us in cleverness. While he was doing the trick he kept murmuring something constantly, as though he were calculating; yet it was certain that what he said did not consist of any reckoning with numbers. But when that well-known friend of ours, after taking a card, looked at it before putting it under a book, Soma said, 'You have confused everything and have spoiled my whole method; nevertheless, the card is the same as the one you drew before, namely, the Two of Flowers [clubs],' and we discovered that this was so.

"And although he showed me certain more wonderful things, still indications were that all of them were the work of a certain art of legerdemain rather than of supernatural beings, or in other words, they were much less miraculous. Nevertheless, the art was too wonderful to be understood by human cogitation. And if he had not asked us at various times to draw different cards, I would have suspected that he had substituted a pack consisting of cards of a single kind, namely, the 'Two of Flowers.' For with that device it would happen that whoever drew a card would always seem to chance upon the same card. But, as I have said, the diversity of the remaining cards precluded that explanation.

"However that may be, I remember reading that this art and these tricks of legerdemain have been imported from the new world where marvelous practitioners exist. It is certain that our ancient authors either did not know them or else kept them secret as is related of Pharaoh and Simon Magus. And although this art is so wonderful, still it is held in no honor, although even a remarkable cook is not without esteem. The reasons are various, it seems to me; first, the art is concerned with useless matters; second, it is practiced by men of low degree" (*De Subtilitate Rerum*, book eighteen).

Still more interesting than methods of cheating are Cardano's descriptions (in chapter seventeen) of the psychological tricks which kibitzers may use to distract a player, making him confused and causing him to lose his judgment and temper: "And there is even greater danger to be feared from the bystanders, if they favor your opponent; and so it comes about that, if you play in a large crowd of people, you can scarcely avoid folly if they are *against* you, or else injustice if they are *for* you. They can injure you in many ways, for example, by giving your opponent open advice and information, which is a twofold evil, since it not only helps their side, but also provokes you to anger and disturbs you; for an angry man, as long as he is angry, is simply insane. Others will annoy you by their disorderly talk, even without giving definite information. Some will purposely consult you on serious business; some will even be so impudent as to provoke you to anger by quarreling with you; others will make fun of you in order to make you angry; others, more modest than these, will indicate to your opponent by foot or by hand that the decision he has made is not the right one; others, again, a little further off, will do this with a nod, perhaps with no other purpose, it may be, than to help him by filling your mind with suspicion. Still others will state falsely how the die has fallen; others will worry you by accusing *you* of such things. For all these reasons it is of the very greatest advantage to you to have your own supporters if you wish to win unjustly; and to play otherwise in the presence of a crowd is simply to waste your money, not to contend for it; for even if nothing of the above happens, suspicion itself disturbs a man and makes him err, so that a suspicious man should not play."

Cardano also warns against professional gamblers. Most likely Cardano himself had a reputation for being a professional gambler in some of the circles in which he associated. His store of information on the subject of trickery is excellent. Whether he personally ever resorted to deceit is a moot question; he certainly never confesses to anything of this kind in his works, but that could not be expected; even for Cardano's outspoken way of writing this would have been an admission which reflected too much on his character. Possibly he did at times rob the robbers; the peculiar method which he employed in his game with Thomas Lezius seems, according to his description, to indicate something of this nature. Cardano ascribes his luck in this case to the science of geomancy; no doubt his opponents must have considered this a quite euphemistic explanation of his persistent run of luck and of his uncanny ability to conjecture the deals of the cards through an entire evening.

In theory at least, Cardano must have been the equal of any gambler he may have encountered, but as everyone knows there is a considerable difference between theory and practice. In the spirit of his systematic analysis such a question cannot be neglected and in one of his chapters Cardano takes up for discussion the topic, "Does a man who knows the theory of the game also play well?" He holds the view that "in those matters which give time for reflection, the same man is both learned and successful, as for instance, in mathematics, jurisprudence and also medicine, for very rarely does a sick man admit no delay." He ridiculed the armchair generals: "It was right for Hannibal to make fun of the philosopher who had never seen a battle line and was discoursing on war." His conclusion in regard to gambling seems to have been that the action is mostly too fast to exercise one's knowledge successfully. "Thus it is with all games which depend on chance, either entirely or together with skill, when they are played rapidly and time is not given for careful thought."

Cardano expended a great deal of careful thought on the subject of games and some of it must have been of utilitarian rather than of a general philosophical nature as it may appear in his book. At times when the welfare of his family actually depended on his surplus from gambling, he was compelled to apply his genius to the task of evolving winning schemes, as for instance, the memory system for cards which he made use of in the game of trappola.

The greatest of all his schemes, as we have already indicated, was the creation of the first principles of probability, and we shall discuss this at greater length in a subsequent chapter. Whether these laws served him well in his gambling we do not know, but Cardano must have been keenly aware of their potentialities. In his *Autobiography* he devotes a chapter to the most important contributions to knowledge which he felt he had made, and here one also finds a line referring to his arguments on chance. However, he was an old and somewhat senile man when he wrote this summary; his memory must have failed him and the statement makes no sense. "I have discovered the reason for astounding facts, for instance, in a thousand throws with a thousand dice which are not loaded there will be at least one monad." Most likely he recalled vaguely his reasoning on the mean outcome, which as we shall see, played such an important role in his probability arguments.

Gamblers are notoriously superstitious, and Cardano not only lived in a superstitious age but he had been infected with occult ideas even in his youth. With such inclinations it is no wonder that *De Ludo Aleae* carries discussions of a number of superstitions, but it must be admitted that Cardano on the whole tempered his beliefs with a good deal of scepticism. The first half of the book shows no trace of the occult, except for the curious belief that a player should preferably sit so that he faces a rapidly rising moon.

When he comes to the discussion of luck Cardano frankly deprecates the possibility that astrologers can be of any help: "Astrologers make claims for themselves, yet I have never seen an astrologer who was lucky at gambling, nor were those lucky who took their advice. The reason is as follows: although, as in all matters of chance, it happens that they occasionally make the right forecast, nevertheless, if they have guessed right (for when they do not guess right, they must lose), then immediately afterward they go very badly wrong, since they become venturesome and lose more from one mistake than they win from forecasting four times in a row. For the path into error is always steeper, and the loss is greater than the gain."

In regard to geomancy he again expressed himself critically: "I have seen others who make their decision with the help of geomancy, but this is an unstable variety and dangerous unless very moderate use is made of its deceptive help. As for the fact that some of them do make correct forecasts, this is to be explained on the grounds that others make still more frequent mistakes. For since there is necessarily some inequality in this respect, one man will be right more often and another less. These statements appear likely to our reason."

He is evidently not wholly convinced and proceeds to submit as an illustration his own application of geomancy against Thomas Lezius so that the reader may judge for himself. After his phenomenal luck his opponent evidently became angry and swore at him: "I believe some demon is advising you or that you know by some enchantment what is going to happen." Cardano, as usual showing little sense of humor, proceeded to interpret the statement literally: "If anyone should say that my Genius was advising me, although apparently he had never yet revealed himself, I will not dispute it; yet, there must have been some art by which the Genius himself had this foreknowledge. On this point (as I have said) I leave the decision to others."

Cardano was always firmly convinced that his own fate was much more remarkable than that of people in general, mainly due to some wonderful supernatural influence: "Now I think it worthy of consideration that this fortune of mine seems to have been something greater than mere chance, since we see in it a beginning, an increase, and a certain continuance so that certain remarkable things happen, as for instance, that two aces appeared twice when defeat could not otherwise be brought about, and other things of the sort. We would also see a decline and then

Rubeus, *Rouge*	*Albus* *Blanc*	*Caput draconis* *Test: de dragõ*	*Cauda draconis* *Queuë de dragon*
Fortuna maior *Fortune maieur*	*Fortuna minor* *Fortune mineur*	*Acquisitio* *Gaing*	*Amißio* *Perte*
Lætitia, *Ioye*	*Tristitia* *Tristesse*	*Puer* *Enfant*	*Puella* *Fille*
Coniunctio *Coniunction*	*Via* *Chemin*	*Populus* *Peuple*	*Carcer* *Prison*

23. A geomancy chart. The diviner would look for such configurations in scattered marks or grains of sand. From Cattan, *Geomancy* (1577).

very often a change, and then great calamity or great fortune, and other things in the same way; in view of all this I should think we ought to decide that there is something in this, although we do not know the law which connects the parts. It is as though you were fated in advance to be enriched or despoiled."

Cardano again concludes this discussion of fortune in play on a somewhat cautious and sceptical note: "Whether the cause of that luck, be it in the conjunction of the stars or in the construction of a certain order of the universe, can affect the cards, which are considered bad or good only according to the judgment of man (since they signify nothing of themselves) is so worthy of doubt that it is easier to find a cause of this fact without that purpose than with it; without it the matter can well be reduced to chance, as in the constitution of the clouds and by scattering beans and the like."

Most enthusiastic gamblers are still full of superstitious convictions: they knock on wood and change to lucky seats; they carry charms and lucky coins; favorite ties and suits and many other items are desirable accessories to successful gambling. Naturally, Cardano also attempts to analyze the effect of such charms and amulets. His conclusions do not appear to be quite consistent in the various statements, but on the whole he seems to have had a firm conviction of their usefulness. "Some people have one thing and other people have other things to report. There are stones which, as they claim, increase the skill of those who wear them and I know the pearl is among them, and similarly other stones which increase boldness, as those which are called Nicolos." The "Nicolos" was the popular name for the stone onyx.

Even today the superstition prevails that the dice should be thrown vigorously; a timid throw rarely wins. Cardano argues the point and decides after some very formal logic that the matter is rather the other way around: "It is because fortune is adverse that the die falls unfavorably, and because the die falls unfavorably, he loses, and because he loses he throws the die timidly."

Cardano goes on to say that luck must depend on the

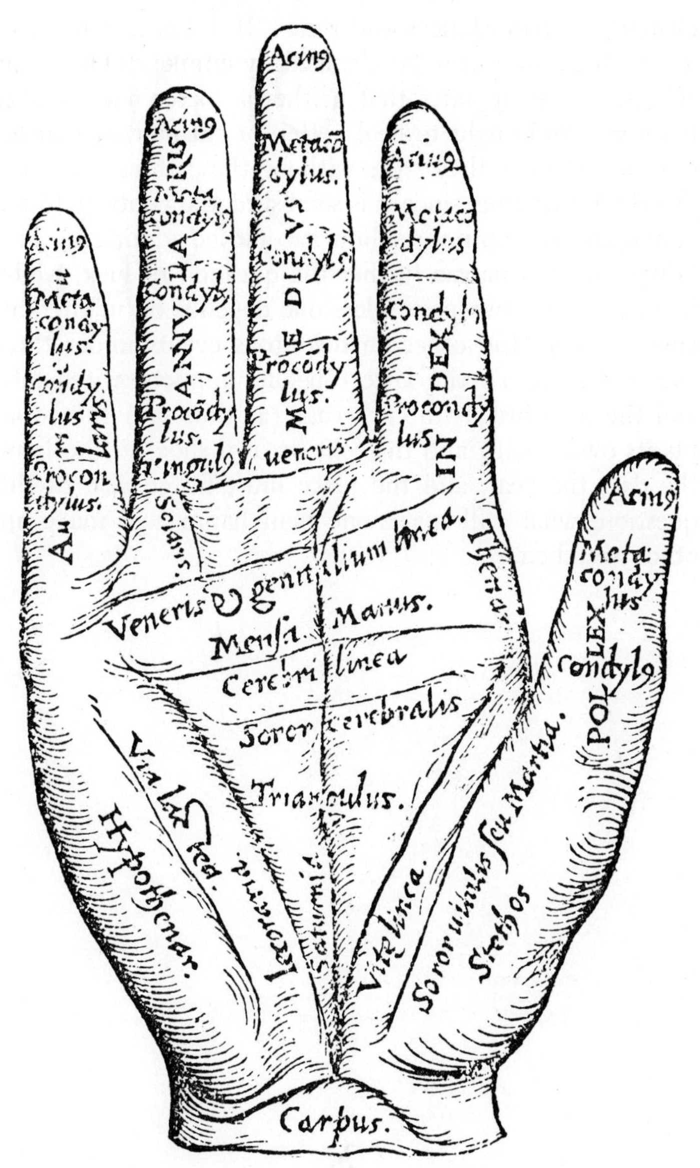

24. A chiromancy chart. From *De Rerum Varietate.*

change in circumstances and time. "If, then, it is to be or not to be, how can it be changed by amulets? This same argument demonstrates that neither a doctor nor a barber nor a war lord ought to heal better, or cut hair, or manage warfare better if they were without these things. Even if this should be true, since it is so absurd and contrary to human opinion, I do not see how it could be admitted." This brings him to analyze further the question of luck, which he divides into two principles: one depends on unalterable laws or plans, the other on fortuitous events under these circumstances. To the latter "belong amulets, witchcrafts and the like; just as in each case (as they say) the sword fits its own sheath and the foot its own shoe, so the hour, the day, the year, and the place must fit; so also in this question, what will make one man happy will make another wretched."

The Science of Gambling

CARDANO's book on games of chance has long been neglected, and this most undeservedly, since it is evident that it is a very important document in the colorful history of science—the first text on the theory of probability. Before Cardano a few weak attempts had been made to find the solution to some special gaming problems, particularly in regard to the chances for various throws on the dice, but the results were erroneous and show no grasp of the basic ideas of probability.

When one takes into account that Cardano's book represents the initial effort in this field, it must be admitted that it is remarkably successful. Even if his achievements had been limited only to the correct chances on dice, it could have been regarded as a great forward step, but Cardano goes much further. He succeeds in formulating certain fundamental principles; he understands to some extent the law of large numbers, and, after some false starts, he is able to derive quite generally the so-called power law for the repetition of events; in addition he solves a number of minor problems on chances by dice, astragals, and cards.

Such accomplishments as these should entitle Cardano to a place of honor in the history of probability, but it is strange to note that in almost every presentation of the development of this branch of mathematics his contributions, if they are mentioned at all, are brushed off with a few superficial remarks. It seems fairly evident that in most cases the writers have made no attempt to examine Cardano's work, or if they have, they have failed to extract the essence of his ideas. Rémond de Montmort wrote one of the first important treatises on probability in the beginning of the eighteenth century, and in his introduction he gives a historical account of the works of his predecessors.

His remarks about Cardano are rather typical of many of the comments one may find later: "Gerolamo Cardano has written a treatise, *De Ludo Aleae,* but here one finds only erudition and moral reflexions."

Only two writers have made more serious efforts to determine the extent of Cardano's discoveries in probability in *De Ludo Aleae*: the first, Isaac Todhunter in his *History of the Mathematical Theory of Probability* (1865), and the second, Moritz Cantor in his encyclopedic history of mathematics (1880). Both of these historians perceived that the frequencies of throws with two or three dice are correct, but this brings their achievements to an end. Todhunter makes various attempts to understand the game of fritillus and especially the table of frequencies which Cardano calculates for it, but he gives up his speculations with the admission that he can see no method of play which will lead to Cardano's figures. He sums up his impressions on a note of hopelessness: "The treatise is so badly written as to be scarcely intelligible."

One can readily concur that there are certain sections of the book which do not yield to understanding by first study; some of Cardano's thoughts only emerge after much detailed analysis and through the use of information on games from contemporary sources—on the game of primero in particular. But such an examination is rewarding; in the end it makes most sections of *De Ludo Aleae* entirely lucid, giving an excellent idea of Cardano's knowledge of gaming, and in particular, the extent of his mastery of probability. Here and there a special statement remains where one must agree with Todhunter that his meaning is scarcely intelligible, but these are so few that they have no influence upon the understanding of the book as a whole.

Cardano's work, naturally, has its shortcomings; it was not to be expected that the theory should spring fully armed from his forehead. Perhaps one may say that there are three principal factors contributing to the obscurity of some of Cardano's mathematical analyses. The first of these is the common complication involved in the reading of all early texts where the lack of a mathematical symbolism makes it necessary to infer all general principles from the treatment of a few special examples.

The second factor is the execrable composition of the book. Cardano confessed himself that he wrote certain parts simply by jotting down notes from time to time as they occurred to him. In this process it is evident that sometimes, when he found that a previous idea was erroneous, he proceeded without warning to the reader to add his new thoughts, not bothering to correct his earlier statements. For instance, in one place where the probabilities for the repetition of an event are under discussion three different solutions for the same problem are given in succession, and he affirms each time that this must be the correct procedure, but only in the third and last attempt does he arrive at the proper method.

The third reason for confusion in the mathematical parts of *De Ludo Aleae* can be found in a fact which hitherto seems to have been unnoticed, namely, that Cardano in some instances in his probability arguments makes use of two entirely different methods. The first is our standard method in probability, the direct count of the various possible cases, and whenever this procedure is used his results are entirely correct. The second method seems to represent Cardano's original approach to probability problems; it may suitably be called a *reasoning on the mean outcome.* It is used in the earlier parts of his probability discussions, often together with the usual method; he resorts to the reasoning on the mean especially in certain more difficult problems where the direct count of cases exceeds his powers. We shall explain the method a little later, but let us only say that it is often easy to apply and under some conditions it gives a fairly good approximation to the correct answer. Cardano himself was aware that the results obtained this way did not agree entirely with his own observations or experiences, but he was not able to give a satisfactory explanation for the discrepancies; some of his obscure statements seem to be concerned precisely with this problem of bringing the two points of view into harmony.

In several places Cardano attempts to grasp the philosophical content of such concepts as chance and luck. To a modern reader his analysis may seem quite superficial and even rather simple-minded in its expression and form. However, it is proper to recall that Cardano's statements represent the initial steps in a discussion which has been continued by mathematicians and philosophers for centuries, indeed to the present day, without complete agreement on a satisfactory definition of what one in modern terminology prefers to call a chance event.

In discussing luck in play in chapter twenty Cardano reasons as follows: "If anyone should throw with a result tending more in one direction than it should and less in another, or else it is always just equal to what it should be, then, in the case of a fair game there will be a reason and a basis for it and it is not a play of chance; but if there are diverse results at every placing of the wagers, then some other factor is present to a greater or lesser extent; there is no rational knowledge of luck to be found in this, though it is necessarily luck."

In chapter twenty-seven Cardano attempts to go deeper into the analysis of the nature of luck. His statements are not clear, but it seems that the gist of his speculations should be interpreted about as follows: he first observes that fortune changes with time, persons, and circumstances and thus may well depend upon what he calls fate. But Cardano does not appear satisfied with this rather tautological presentation and proceeds to dissect the problem further:

"Let us therefore examine what this luck is and on what

principle it depends; certainly it seems to me to be a disposition of affairs in accordance with or adverse to the will or plan of a man; so that no matter how you act, the matter turns out well or badly, or agrees with human plans or does not agree. Good fortune is two-fold, like force and guile in human affairs, and it may suit our plan or deceive us. For if I stay at home or do not stay, it can turn out very badly either way; but whatever happens, we are subject to the authority of the Prince. So it is also in games. Therefore, there are two kinds of happenings and nonhappenings, one of them absolute and the other relative to plan or judgment."

In brief, Cardano's idea seems to be that luck and fortune pertain to human plans and expectations, but no matter how these plans are laid, there are general laws of nature or absolute rules of the game, "the authority of the Prince," which cannot be violated. He continues to say that once a plan is made its luck may differ in two ways, one openly, perhaps one may say, for lack of judgment, and the other secretly, where the outcome may be unfavorable by pure chance in spite of good judgment:

"These matters are treated in the books about fate, but as far as the present question is concerned, it is sufficient to say here that fortune is changed by some principle, like a plan is changed, sometimes openly, as when I should go to war and experience a different fortune than if I should go on a journey or remain at home; but sometimes secretly as in gambling, as when I should shake more or less, and a different point should come forth with each different impetus. Therefore, fortune works secretly in a twofold way, either by changing the plan from which action results, or else by means of an event which is fortuitous in comparison with the existing circumstances."

Cardano's illustration is quaint and in the spirit of the Renaissance: "For example, I have an enemy, and thus his bad luck is part of my plan; but if his power should be increased by the marriage of his daughter, this pertains to luck and has nothing to do with my plan."

Cardano's more technical studies on probability theory begin in chapter nine where, as a preliminary, throws with a single die are treated. He concludes this first section with the remark that "these facts contribute a great deal to understanding but hardly anything to practical play." He refers presumably to the fact that none of the games in use at the time were played with a single die; it is also true that here we begin to find the basic concepts which pervade all the subsequent arguments.

On a single die there are six "equally likely cases" in modern probability terminology. This Cardano expresses by saying that the "circuit" is six and in general his term circuit can be translated as "the total number of equally likely cases." Cardano also counts correctly for throws with two dice; each face on one die must be combined with each of the six faces on the second, so that here the circuit is $6 \times 6 = 36$. Later he finds analogously that for throws with three dice the "circuit consists of $6 \times 6 \times 6 = 216$ cases."

In the subsequent chapters Cardano counts up the number of favorable cases for many different outcomes on the dice, and when c is the number in the circuit he computes the fraction

$$p = f/c$$

which represents ordinary probability exactly as it is defined and used today.

The meaning of this probability in actual play Cardano expresses in chapter fourteen in formulating his *general law of wagers*: "So there is one general rule, namely, that we should consider the whole circuit and the number of those casts which represents in how many ways the favorable result can occur and compare that number to the remainder of the circuit, and according to that proportion should the mutual wagers be laid so that one may contend on equal terms."

To Cardano there is another concept which is just as fundamental as the circuit. This is *equality*, which represents *half the number* in the circuit. For instance, for a single die he says, "one half of the total number of faces always represents equality." For two dice equality is 18, half of 36, and for three dice Cardano affirms similarly that the circuit is 216 and equality 108. As a consequence, in computing the probabilities Cardano systematically determines two fractions, namely, first the ordinary probability obtained by determining the quotient of the favorable cases f with the circuit c as before, and secondly the proportion of favorable cases with respect to equality $e = c/2$. Thus he usually quotes two fractions

$$p = f/c, \qquad p_e = f/e = 2 \times f/c = 2p$$

one the ordinary probability and the other its double value, which we shall call the *equality proportion.*

This certainly appears somewhat strange according to modern views and one may be curious to determine the reasons why Cardano is led to the introduction of the second concept. There are undoubtedly several contributing circumstances, but the following may have weighed most heavily.

When a player has a probability p of winning some price P, then the amount he should justly feel entitled to in advance, his *mathematical expectation* as we now say, or the correct amount to bet, should be $E = p \cdot P$. For instance, if he has a chance of 1 in 6 to win, his expectation is $1/6\ P$. But Cardano evidently has the practical game in mind and he seems to assume that usually there are only two opponents competing. Customarily, each will stake the same amount A so that the whole pot is $P = 2A$. When a player considers how much he has won or lost it is natural to relate it not to the whole pot 2A but to his own stake A. In terms of such a measure his expectation becomes

$$E = pP = 2p \cdot A = p_e \cdot A$$

so that the equality proportion or the double probability becomes the natural factor measuring loss or gain.

In a fair game for the two opponents the number of favorable and unfavorable cases must be the same and each player has the same probability

$$p = q = \tfrac{1}{2}$$

This means that each player has *equality* in his favorable cases, so that the corresponding equality proportions are

$$p_e = q_e = 1$$

and Cardano expresses this simply by saying that "there is equality."

As we shall see a little later on, there is also another problem analyzed by Cardano in which the same equality proportion appears as the natural measure rather than the probability.

In his first discussion of probability problems in chapter eleven Cardano resorts to the method which we, for want of a better name, shall call *reasoning on the mean.* In many of his later considerations it also plays an important role.

To explain Cardano's point of view let us take the throws with a single die where he first introduces the principle. When a die is thrown, each of its six faces should in the long run appear approximately equally often. Consequently, Cardano reasons, in six throws usually each of the six faces will have appeared once; this is not entirely correct in a single series "since the circuit may be deceptive" but in the long run the reasoning should be approximately correct.

On this basis, the chance that a six will have appeared in a single throw is $p = 1/6$, since one throw is 1/6 of the circuit. One could also state this by saying that a single throw produces 1/6 of the desired point. Then, Cardano argues similarly, two throws will produce

$$2 \cdot \tfrac{1}{6} = \tfrac{1}{3}$$

of the point one wishes and in three throws one should expect

$$3 \cdot \tfrac{1}{6} = \tfrac{1}{2}$$

of the point, so that he concludes, "The chances are equal that a given point will turn up in three throws, for the total circuit is completed in six."

If one continues the argument for a single die, it should be fairly certain that the point has appeared once in six throws. It is evident how this argument would run in general: if there are f favorable cases in a circuit of length c, then a single trial will produce on the average

$$p = f/c$$

successes. Two trials will produce $2 \cdot f/c$ successes, etc. This type of reasoning leads to the correct value for a single throw or a single trial, but in general it will produce erroneous results, as one readily sees. For a small number of trials and relatively small probabilities the approximation is fairly satisfactory, but for higher numbers of throws the discrepancy may be considerable. For instance, it implies, when applied to six throws, that a six will have appeared with certainty and for more than six throws it even leads to probabilities greater than unity.

For the understanding of several of the subsequent sections in *De Ludo Aleae* it is essential to keep both of these two methods constantly in mind: the correct probability counts, and the reasoning on the mean. We shall presently compare the two in some detail for the special case of throws with two or three dice, because exactly at this point lies the source of an essential error which causes confusion in several later sections, particularly in the computations regarding the game of Fritillus.

Already for two throws with a die or one throw with two dice, there is a discrepancy between the two methods, although here it is quite small. Out of the thirty-six possible throws of the two dice there are actually eleven cases which include a six, namely, six throws with a six on the first die, and six throws with a six on the second, but in these twelve throws the case where there is a six on both has been counted twice so that the total is eleven. Thus the probability for at least one six in two casts is

$$p = \frac{11}{36}$$

as Cardano also computes later. The reasoning on the mean gives

$$p' = \frac{1}{3} = \frac{12}{36}$$

as we saw above.

For three throws with one die, or, equivalently, one throw with three dice, the discrepancy is somewhat greater. By combining the six faces on the three dice one obtains 216 cases, as we have already noted. To count up those casts which include at least one six we observe that, if the first six occurs on the first die, the other two dice may show any face, so that we have $6 \times 6 = 36$ cases. If the first six appears on the second die, there are five possible faces on the first die and when these are combined with an arbitrary face on the third die it yields $5 \times 6 = 30$ cases. Finally, the six may not show until the third die; then any one of five faces may appear on the two first dice so that we now have $5 \times 5 = 25$ cases. This leads to a total of

$$36 + 30 + 25 = 91$$

favorable cases for obtaining at least one six in three throws; the corresponding probability is therefore

$$p = \frac{91}{216}$$

The argument on the mean, as we saw, led to a different value, namely,

$$p' = 3 \times \frac{1}{6} = \frac{108}{216}$$

The difference between these two results affords a very

plausible explanation for some of Cardano's following figures. It appears that Cardano, at least to begin with, accepts the reasoning on the mean and consequently also the figure 108, that is, equality, for obtaining at least one six in three throws with a die. Not until the middle of chapter fourteen does he suddenly realize that he is wrong and that in one throw with three dice or three throws with a single die, the number of cases for the appearance of a specific point is 91 and not 108: "For the ace does not have a number of favorable throws equal to half the whole circuit, but the odds are 91 to 125." But from this point on Cardano works exclusively with the correct figure 91 and his results are entirely correct.

After a digression on Aristotle's views on gambling Cardano returns in earnest to his probability studies in chapter eleven. Here he concentrates on questions concerning throws with two dice. He first counts up six casts

$$(1,1), \ldots, (6,6)$$

of doublets, that is, throws, with equal faces on the two dice, while he finds that there are fifteen combinations

$$(1,2), \ldots, (5,6)$$

where the points are different. Each of these combinations must be counted twice, since for instance (1,2) with an ace on the first and a deuce on the second die is counted as a different throw from the reverse order (2,1). Thus Cardano arrives at a total of thirty cases of the second category. This shows that the probability for a doublet like (1,1) is $p = 1/36$, and for a throw with two different points like (1,2) it is $p = 2/36 = 1/18$.

However, the main problem in chapter eleven is the same which appeared more than a century later in the discussions between de Méré and Pascal. It is often referred to as "de Méré's problem," but the account in *De Ludo Aleae* shows that there is much greater justification for calling it "Cardano's problem."

In all generality the problem may be formulated as follows: some play or experiment shall be repeated a number of times until a successful outcome appears; one wants to determine how many trials a player shall be allowed so that there may be an even chance for him to obtain success. In the main example cited both by Cardano and de Méré one keeps throwing two dice until a double six or some other particular point shows up. It seems to have been a fairly popular gambling proposition to bet on the number of throws a player will require and it is still in use in various forms of dice games.

The exact solution of this problem exceeds Cardano's powers and he resorts to the reasoning on the mean to arrive at some approximate answer. In the general situation his argument would presumably run as follows: let p be the probability that the particular event shall happen in a single trial, for instance, that one shall obtain two sixes in a throw with two dice. Then in a single trial the event will on the average appear p times; consequently in n attempts it will on the average appear

$$N_n = n \cdot p$$

times. If this number were equal to ½ there should presumably be equality, that is, one should fail or succeed with equal chance in having at least one favorable outcome. Therefore, the corresponding number n_o of attempts, the *critical number* as we say presently, should be determined by

$$n_o = \frac{1}{2p} = \frac{1}{p_e} \qquad (1)$$

Here again we see the double probability or the equality proportion make its appearance and this may have served as a confirmation of Cardano's view that it should be considered a fundamental quantity in measuring chance.

Cardano applies the result which is expressed in Equation (1) to several examples. If one throws two dice until two sixes appear, then $p = 1/36$ and the critical number becomes $n_0 = 18$. The correct value lies between 24 and 25 so that Cardano's approximation is not especially good. Next, in throwing until one obtains some particular unequal point like (1,2), one has $p = 1/18$ and consequently, by Equation (1), $n_0 = 9$; the correct value, as can be demonstrated, lies a little above 12. Finally, when one throws a single die until a six appears, we have $p = 1/6$ and correspondingly $n_0 = 3$, a result which Cardano has already mentioned in chapter nine. This value is fairly satisfactory since the correct figure lies between 3 and 4. It may well have been this result, conforming to his gambling experience, which brought Cardano to place so much faith in his reasoning on the mean; also in other instances one can see that he attempts to generalize on evidence which is very slim indeed.

In the third section of chapter eleven Cardano mentions the fact which we have already verified that there are eleven throws with two dice which include at least one ace. Cardano states that this is a little more than half of equality, since the circuit is 36, equality is 18, and half of equality is 9. He continues, that in two throws with two dice the chances of getting at least one ace each time lies between 1/4 and 1/6 of equality, that is, the corresponding probability lies between 1/8 and 1/12. He does not indicate how he arrives at this result, but the exact value is

$$p = \left(\tfrac{11}{36}\right)^2 = \tfrac{1}{10.7}$$

so that his statement is correct, although the limits he indicates give only rough estimates.

In the fourth and last section of chapter eleven Cardano touches upon the probabilities for three throws with two dice. In regard to the probability that each throw shall include at least one ace he restricts himself to the statement that it "falls far short of the whole circuit." The actual probability is small, namely,

$$p = \left(\tfrac{11}{36}\right)^3 = \tfrac{1,331}{46,656} \sim \tfrac{1}{35}\,^*$$

Next Cardano states that obtaining an ace at least twice in three throws differs from equality by 1/12. The correct probability according to well-known rules is

$$p = 3 \cdot \left(\tfrac{11}{36}\right)^2 \cdot \tfrac{25}{36} + \left(\tfrac{11}{36}\right)^3 = \tfrac{10,406}{46,656} \sim 0.22$$

which is quite different from equality or $p = 0.5$. However, it is evident from Cardano's subsequent remarks that he has in mind the reasoning on the mean and one arrives at his result by the following argument: when the whole circuit of thirty-six throws with the two dice is performed, there should result eleven cases with at least one ace. If one makes only three throws one should expect

$$3 \cdot \tfrac{11}{36} = \tfrac{11}{12}$$

such casts. There would have been equality for obtaining two throws with an ace out of three if this number had turned out to be unity, thus proportionally the chances fall short of equality by 1/12. Cardano realizes that the results are not entirely satisfactory when he concludes, "this knowledge is based on conjecture, which yields only an approximation and the reckoning is not exact in these details; yet it happens in the case of many circuits that the matter falls out very close to conjecture."

Chapter twelve of *De Ludo Aleae* is devoted to the enumeration of throws with three dice. There are six throws with all three faces alike

$$(1,1,1), \ldots, (6,6,6)$$

as before. The number of types of throws with a doublet and one different face like (1,1,2) is $6 \times 5 = 30$ since the doublet can be taken in six ways and the different point

* Here as in the following the symbol $\sim$ is used in the mathematical sense "nearly equal to."

subsequently in five ways. But the three permutations, for instance,

$$(1,1,2), \qquad (1,2,1), \qquad (2,1,1)$$

must be considered to be different so that the total is $3 \times 30 = 90$. Finally, throws like (1,2,3) where all faces are different have twenty cases since there are twenty ways of selecting three different points out of six; but again each of these gives rise to six different permutations, for instance,

$$(1,2,3), \qquad (1,3,2), \qquad (2,1,3)$$
$$(2,3,1), \qquad (3,1,2), \qquad (3,2,1)$$

so that there is a total of $6 \times 20 = 120$ throws with different faces. The total circuit is therefore

$$6 + 90 + 120 = 216$$

and equality half of this, 108, as we mentioned before.

In the second section this whole analysis is repeated with a few more details and Cardano observes further that a triplet like (1,1,1) has a 1/108 chance of equality while a doublet (1,1,2) has the chance

$$\frac{3}{108} = \frac{1}{36}$$

of equality. He compares this with the case of two dice where a doublet is 1/18 of equality. But the concluding statement, "therefore in comparison with the former it will occur three times as often," is ambiguous. It is only correct if he refers to the previous discussion of triplets and doublets by three dice, but the context seems to indicate that he compares doublets by two dice to doublets or triplets by three dice and in this case the words "three times" should be replaced either by "twice" or "six times."

In the third section Cardano studies in how many ways a throw like (1,2) on two dice can be completed to a throw with three dice. By adjoining an ace one gets the throws

$$(1,1,2), \qquad (1,2,1), \qquad (2,1,1)$$

and taking a deuce one gets similarly three throws

$$(1,2,2), \qquad (2,1,2), \qquad (2,2,1)$$

for a total of six. But one could also add one of the four points different from one and two and this gives $4 \times 6 = 24$ throws. Thus there is a total of $6 + 24 = 30$ cases arising from $(1,2)$.

The sense of the brief fourth section cannot be explained satisfactorily; there may possibly be some misstatement in the figures. Since Cardano compares throws with two and three dice, one should naturally expect him to compute the proportion of throws including the pair $(1,2)$ and this would give

$$\frac{30}{216} = \frac{5}{36}$$

which is "almost 1/6 but not quite."

The remaining section presents no particular difficulties. A throw like $(1,2,3)$ has the probability

$$\frac{6}{216} = \frac{1}{36}$$

and this is the same as the probability for a doublet on two dice. At this stage, after these studies of throws with three dice, it seems peculiar that Cardano still has not discovered that there are 91 throws which include a particular point, say an ace. He repeats the argument on the mean and again arrives at the erroneous figure 108. The situation is similar to that on two dice, he maintains. Here the probability for a particular point was 11/36, and since

$$\frac{11}{36} \cdot 3 = \frac{33}{36} \sim 1$$

the circuit is completed in three throws and equality for a particular point is 1½ throws, which is not bad as an approximation.

In chapter thirteen Cardano turns to the probabilities for the various dice points by throws with two or three dice. He enumerates the results both for the game of Sors and for Fritillus. Sors may perhaps best be translated as outcome or point and refers only to the probability of obtaining a particular total on the dice. Fritillus, however, as we have seen, is most likely the game of tables or backgammon.

Cardano's discussion of the points on two dice corresponds to the following table:

$$12 = 6 + 6$$
$$11 = 6 + 5 = 5 + 6$$
$$10 = 6 + 4 = 5 + 5 = 4 + 6$$
$$9 = 6 + 3 = 5 + 4 = 4 + 5 = 3 + 6$$
$$8 = 6 + 2 = 5 + 3 = 4 + 4 = 3 + 5 = 2 + 6$$
$$7 = 6 + 1 = 5 + 2 = 4 + 3 = 3 + 4 = 2 + 5 = 1 + 6$$
$$6 = 5 + 1 = 4 + 2 = 3 + 3 = 2 + 4 = 1 + 5$$
$$5 = 4 + 1 = 3 + 2 = 2 + 3 = 1 + 4$$
$$4 = 3 + 1 = 2 + 2 = 1 + 3$$
$$3 = 2 + 1 = 1 + 2$$
$$2 = 1 + 1$$

This gives the table of cases

Point	2	3	4	5	6	7	8	9	10	11	12
Sors	1	2	3	4	5	6	5	4	3	2	1
Fritillus	12	13	14	15	16	6	5	4	3	2	1

In the text Cardano computes the probabilities and also the equality proportions for the various throws with two dice and in some cases simpler approximation fractions are given, presumably with a view to the practical application in gambling.

In Fritillus with two dice it seems evident that the rules are, as often at present in backgammon, that the player has his choice either to move one man as many steps as the total on the two dice or to move two different men according to the point on each separate die. Since Cardano has already found that by two dice there are eleven cases which include a particular point, he obtains the Fritillus cases for the various points simply by adding eleven to the figures for the points from one to six. It should be noted that here the single point one can occur in eleven cases, while the points above six can only appear as a sum on two dice.

The next task is to compute the number of cases and

probabilities for three dice. It may be emphasized that already these results for the dice points represent a notable achievement since Cardano's tables antedate by far all known correct studies of dice probabilities. The only later study which may have originated in the same century is Galileo's fragment *Considerazione sopra il Giuoco dei Dadi*, which he wrote for the benefit of some of the gambling noblemen at the court in Florence. It is undated, but it cannot have been composed much earlier than 1600 and may well have appeared later. After that one finds no such tables until the first printed presentation in Christian Huygens' book *De Ratiociniis in Ludo Aleae* (*Computations in Games of Chance*) which was published in 1657, probably more than a century after Cardano's studies.

Cardano's computations of the number of cases by three dice are straightforward and not in need of any comment. But parallel with the straight throws he also derives the number of cases for the game of Fritillus with three dice. These results, as we mentioned, represent enough of an enigma to have brought to a halt Todhunter's efforts to decipher Cardano's work. We shall have to find an interpretation of the way in which the figures may have arisen.

It must be observed first that Cardano's table of frequencies for Fritillus in chapter thirteen is somewhat at variance with the values which he states in the text. Since the numerals, as is customary with Cardano, have been written out fully in letters in the text, this seems a more reliable source and thus the errors should most likely be misprints in the tables. After such corrections the table of frequencies for Fritillus runs as follows:

TABLE FOR FRITILLUS

Point	1	2	3	4	5	6	7	8	9
Frequency	108	111	115	120	126	133	33	36	37
Point	10	11	12	13	14	15	16	17	18
Frequency	36	33	26	21	15	10	6	3	1

Here the frequency for the point 4 has been corrected to 120 from 125 and for the point 11 to 33 from 38.

We are now faced with the problem of reconstructing the rules for the moves of the men in Fritillus from these figures. After having made various attempts in this direction I have come to the conviction that the following regulations for the game are most natural and in the closest agreement with Cardano's statements.

After having performed his throw with the three dice a player has the choice of moving one, two, or three men according to these rules:

1. The sum on all three dice may be used for the move of a single man.

2a. In the case of a doublet, that is, two equal and one different as for instance (3,3,4), the sum $3 + 4$ of the two different points may be used for one man and the remaining point 3 in the doublet for a second man.

2b. The sum of the two equal points in a doublet can only be used for one man if the third point is a 6, for instance in (4,4,6) one man may be moved $4 + 4 = 8$ steps.

3. Three men can always be moved separately according to the 3 points showing on the dice.

According to these rules a man can only be moved from thirteen to eighteen steps when one uses the sum on three dice, and the figures in the table above show exactly the frequencies for these points on three dice.

Cardano makes separate comments about the frequencies of the points from 7 to 12 and these are in agreement with rules 2a and 2b. These points can only be obtained as the sum on two or three dice, and when one counts up the possible cases according to 1, 2a, and 2b, Cardano's figures emerge as in the table.

This leaves us only with the points from 1 to 6 to be examined. These may be obtained on a single die, as well as in some cases as the sum on two and three dice. According to rules 1 and 2 one may readily compute in how many ways each of them can be represented as such a sum. If the figures obtained in this manner are subtracted from those in the table, for each point from 1 to 6, one should arrive at the number of cases in which this point occurs at least on one die in throws with three dice. When this calculation is performed one finds that the rest is everywhere the same, namely, 108 cases for each point. Although this figure is not correct, as we have seen, it is in complete harmony with Cardano's stand up to this point, since so far, instead of the correct number 91, he accepts everywhere the erroneous number 108 to which he was originally led by the reasoning on the mean. He probably computed his table by first taking the cases according to rules 1 and 2, then adding 108 from 1 to 6 just as he added the fixed eleven cases for Fritillus with two dice.

In chapter fourteen Cardano first turns to the question of the probabilities for obtaining some particular choice of points by the throws of the dice. Theoretically this is of interest in showing that Cardano was familiar with some of the simplest additive properties of the probabilities.

He begins by studying throws with two dice. Here the cases for obtaining some particular point, say an ace, number 11 as we have mentioned several times. But the number of cases for obtaining either an ace or a deuce is not $2 \times 11 = 22$ but only 20, since the throws (1,2) and (2,1) would be counted twice. Similarly, for either ace, deuce, or trey "there will not be 29, nor 31, but 27," and Cardano computes the correct table for the various choices:

COMBINATIONS OF POINTS FOR TWO DICE

	Number	*Total*
Cases for 1 point	11	11
Additional for: 2	9	20
3	7	27
4	5	32
5	3	35
6	1	36

In the subsequent sections Cardano uses this table to give the proper odds in a few very simple examples. He mentions that the probability for obtaining any one of the points one, two, or three by two dice is

$$\frac{27}{36} = \frac{3}{4}$$

so that the odds are three to one; for the points up to four the probability is

$$\frac{32}{36} = \frac{8}{9}$$

with odds of eight to one. For obtaining one of the throws (1,1) and (2,2) the odds are seventeen to one.

In section four of chapter fourteen Cardano tackles the same problems for three dice and attempts first to reason by analogy from the case of two dice. He observes that in the first column of the preceding table the increases for each additional point form an arithmetic series with the constant difference 2. According to his previous views the number of cases for a single point on three dice should be 108 and so he proposes to determine an arithmetic series beginning with 108 which should serve a similar purpose for the determination of the frequencies by combinations of points on three dice.

Cardano refers to such a table which was to be found in the margin of the book, but this table as well as a number of other computations which should be included in the margin are evidently omitted in the publication of his works. But it is clear that the results which this process produced must have made him reflect and examine the matter more closely, for immediately afterward he realized that there was an error and jotted down the observation, "the ace does not have a number of favorable throws equal to half the whole circuit, but the odds are 91 to 125." From now on only this correct figure is used.

After this discovery Cardano derives the table of values for any choice of points on three dice analogous to the previous table for two dice.

COMBINATIONS OF POINTS FOR THREE DICE

	Number	Total
Cases for 1 point	91	91
Additional for: 2	61	152
3	37	189
4	19	208
5	7	215
6	1	216

He plays a little with these figures and discovers that here the figures in the first column no longer form a simple arithmetic series, but an arithmetic series of second order.

Next one finds the statement of the general rule about wagers: odds should be established in the proportion of the favorable to the unfavorable cases in the circuit. Cardano evidently places great weight on this rule and proclaims rather pompously that he has made it available even to those who have not studied the classical philosophers: "I have wished this matter not to lie hidden because many people, not understanding Aristotle, have been deceived, and with loss."

One of the most interesting parts of *De Ludo Aleae* is an analysis of the probabilities for the repetition of an event. Here Cardano succeeds in all generality, but only after several trials, in establishing the power law for such probabilities. The section is complicated in form; in line with Cardano's whole method of composition the first erroneous attempts are included as well as the final correct arguments. It illustrates well his method of exploring the situation by trial and error, beginning with the very simplest cases.

The first discussion of repeated events occurs in the last section of chapter fourteen. The odds for obtaining at least one ace in a throw with three dice are 91 to 125. To find the odds for an ace in each of two successive such casts, Cardano seems to follow a common gambling rule and sets them equal to 91^2 to 125^2, or 8,281 to 15,625. This he approximates as 1 to 2 so that his probability value is

$p' = 0.33$, which is almost double the correct figure $p = 0.18$. The odds for aces in each of three successive throws he takes analogously to be 91^3 to 125^3, or 753,571 to 1,953,125. This is approximated as 2 to 5; Cardano's probability value in this case is $p' = 0.28$, which differs greatly from the true value $p = 0.07$.

But in resuming his study of these questions in chapter fifteen Cardano admits that "this reasoning seems to be false." To make the error quite evident he takes the special case of equality, that is, some event where the odds are 1 to 1, for instance, throwing an even or an odd point on a single die. According to his previous rule "the odds for obtaining an even point twice in succession should be 1^2 to 1^2, for three times 1^3 to 1^3 and, in general, there should be equal odds for obtaining an even point any number of times, "which is most absurd."

The realization of his error makes Cardano tackle the case of equal odds again in the second section of chapter fifteen. His statements seem to indicate that he believes that, when one throws a die three times, there is only one case which produces all even points but eight cases (instead of seven) in which there is at least one odd point.

Misled by this mistake Cardano again goes off the track in attempting to generalize. When there is equality in a single throw, the general rule, as one knows, should be that the odds are $2^n - 1$ to 1 for repetition in each of n casts. But Cardano states the odds as $n^2 - 1$ to 1 and this is only true for $n = 2$, where the odds for obtaining an even point twice in succession are 3 to 1. From his formula he computes the chances for three, four, or five consecutive repetitions of an even point to be respectively 8 to 1, 15 to 1, and 24 to 1. In connection with the last case he seems to believe that the argument on the mean should show that, if one throws 125 times, there should be five sequences of five consecutive even throws. However, at this stage it is apparent that Cardano begins to doubt the consequences of his own formula and the section ends on a note of confusion. For $n = 20$ he computes the odds produced by the formula not as 399 to 1 but as 7,999 to 1, obtained by using the third power instead of the square; but he is still not convinced that, even in this much larger number of throws, one can reasonably expect a sequence of twenty successive even throws to appear.

After these failures Cardano realizes that guesses will not lead him to his goal and that he can find no satisfactory solution to his problem without clarifying its underlying logical principles. His great mathematical ability manifests itself again in the subsequent analyses. In the first example he assumes that the chance of success in a single trial is $p = 3/4$, as for instance the chance of obtaining one of the points one, two, or three in a throw with three dice. However, in order to avoid all extraneous considerations, he constructs a corresponding ideal case: assuming that one uses a talus or astragal (that is, a prism with 4 sides) with faces named *a, b, c,* and *d* and with *a, b,* and *c* signifying odd or success and *d* denoting even or failure, the probability for a success is then $p = 3/4$, as before.

Cardano takes first two astragals A and B and tabulates the various cases for each. Since the faces on A are combined with those on B, the circuit or total number of possible cases is $4^2 = 16$. Two successes are obtained only by combining a success on A with a success on B so that there are $3^2 = 9$ favorable cases and the remaining 7 cases are unfavorable.

Similarly, when the basic probability is $p = 2/3$ Cardano uses a prism with three sides of which two are favorable and one unfavorable; here the total number of cases for a combined throw of two tali is $3^2 = 9$ and among these are $2^2 = 4$ favorable ones for success on both. Again, when $p = 4/5$ the prism must have five sides of which four are favorable; with two throws there will be $5^2 = 25$ possible cases of which $4^2 = 16$ are favorable for two successes.

In later treatises on probability, particularly in the eighteenth century, this device of using a prism or die with an arbitrary number of sides to represent an arbitrary probability was much in use; it is of interest to note that the technique was already familiar to Cardano. Still later, as one knows, it was replaced by the urn scheme where one was supposed to draw white or black balls out of urns in which they were mixed in varying proportions.

From the studies which we just mentioned Cardano realizes that the correct general rule must be: if the total number of cases on one die is n and the favorable cases are f, then the odds for obtaining two successive successes are

$$f^2 \text{ to } n^2 - f^2$$

In more standard terms, the probability is

$$p_2 = p^2$$

He proceeds to establish that for three successes the formula should be

$$p_3 = p^3$$

and analogously for four throws.

This makes it clear that Cardano in general mastered the power formula

$$p_n = p^n \tag{2}$$

for obtaining n successes in n independent repetitions of an experiment. Equation (2) itself might therefore most appropriately be named "Cardano's formula."

The remaining sections of chapter fifteen are devoted to examples concerning the applications of the Formula (2) and they are all entirely correct; the numerical computations in the margin to which Cardano refers in several instances are missing.

In the first example Cardano notes that on a single die the probability of obtaining an ace or a deuce is $p = 1/3$. Consequently, the probabilities for obtaining these points two, three, or four times in succession are respectively

$$p_2 = \tfrac{1}{9}, \qquad p_3 = \tfrac{1}{27}, \qquad p_4 = \tfrac{1}{81}$$

The next example concerns throws with two dice and here it has already been shown previously that the probability of at least one of the points one, two, or three appearing is

$$p = \frac{27}{36} = \frac{3}{4}$$

Cardano wants to determine the probability that each of three throws shall include at least one of these points. It is peculiar that in performing these calculations Cardano does not make use of the reduced form of the probability fraction but takes the cubes of the numbers 27 and 36. This leads him to the result

$$p_3 = \frac{19{,}683}{46{,}656}$$

which, as he states, lies between 3/7 and 2/5. The reduced probability $p = 3/4$ gives the simpler exact value

$$p_3 = \frac{27}{64}$$

In his final example Cardano takes throws with three dice; the probability for an ace to be included in such a throw is

$$p = \frac{91}{216}$$

He determines the probability that an ace shall be included three times in succession as

$$p_3 = \frac{753{,}571}{9{,}324{,}125}$$

which yields the approximate odds of 12 to 1.

Cardano has every reason to be proud of his general Formula (2) and his concluding statement shows that he feels that he has achieved full clarity: "From this it is clear that any other reasoning is not satisfactory, but that this reasoning is generally true."

Cardano's principal chapters on probability end here, but there still remain several sections of *De Ludo Aleae* in which probability questions are treated. Several of these can be found in the last few chapters where the astragal or talus games of classical antiquity are described. It has been mentioned that Cardano had drawn some of the general information on these subjects from a prior work by Celio Calcagnini, but the probability studies are entirely his own.

The tali or astragals are small bones from the hind legs of sheep or goats. In their natural state they are somewhat irregular in shape but may be described very roughly as four-sided prisms with rounded ends. The four sides differ sufficiently in their appearance to make it possible to distinguish among them, and so the early tali were not marked. Later on artificial astragals with plane faces came into use and it became customary to indicate the various sides with the Greek letters α, γ, δ, and ϛ or 1, 3, 4, and 6. Among them the one was usually known as the *dog*.

Cardano's numerous quotations, mostly from Calcagnini, amply confirm the abundance of references to games with astragals in classical sources. However, in Cardano's time the tali seem to have become obsolete and the tradition about the game was probably mostly kept alive through the study of the ancient authors.

The Greeks and Romans usually played with four astragals, and each type of throw had its particular and peculiar name. Our information about the exact form of these various throws is scant, and one has the impression that several of the commentaries on the classical texts have indulged in considerable guesswork. Even Cardano's own terminology, which is not very extensive, may in some instances be open to question. Only on one point do all sources agree: the *Venus* throw appeared when all four astragals showed a different face.

Cardano first enumerates the various types of throws with four astragals. The following table illustrates his classifications:

TYPES OF THROWS WITH FOUR ASTRAGALS

Type I	(1,1,1,1),	(3,3,3,3),	(4,4,4,4),	(6,6,6,6)
Type II	(1,1,1,3),	(1,1,1,4),	(1,1,1,6)	
	(3,3,3,1),	(3,3,3,4),	(3,3,3,6)	
	(4,4,4,1),	(4,4,4,3),	(4,4,4,6)	
	(6,6,6,1),	(6,6,6,3),	(6,6,6,4)	
Type III	(1,1,3,3),	(1,1,4,4),	(1,1,6,6)	
	(3,3,4,4),	(3,3,6,6),	(4,4,6,6)	
Type IV	(1,1,3,4),	(1,1,3,6),	(1,1,4,6)	
	(3,3,1,4),	(3,3,1,6),	(3,3,4,6)	
	(4,4,1,3),	(4,4,1,6),	(4,4,3,6)	
	(6,6,1,3),	(6,6,1,4),	(6,6,3,4)	
Type V	(1,2,3,4)			

Thus, as Cardano indicates, there are

$$4 + 12 + 6 + 12 + 1 = 35$$

different types of throws.

However, for the count of probability cases this enumeration is not the proper one to use. In throws with four astragals the four faces on each must be combined with those on all the others so that there is a total of $4^4 = 256$ possible cases. Correspondingly, in the table above each type of throw must be counted in all its permutations. Cardano notes that the Venus throw in v has 24 permutations and thus it occurs 6 times more often than any throw with 4 alike. Each throw in II has 4 permutations giving a total of 48; in III the permutations number 6 resulting in 36 throws; and finally the throws in IV may vary in 12 ways so that the total is 144. Cardano checks the figures by the addition

$$4 + 24 + 48 + 36 + 144 = 256$$

He computes the probability for the Venus throw to be

$$p = \frac{24}{256} = \frac{3}{32}$$

which is very close to 1/11. The *Stesichorus* throw is known to have the value eight, derived from the fact that the tomb of this poet was octagonal in shape. Cardano assumes that the throw was (1,1,3,3), which possibly is correct, and states that it is rare since it has only six permutations.

Among the most interesting sections from the point of view of mathematical theory are the discussions of the expected or mean number which Cardano includes in chapter thirty-two, the last in the *Ludo Aleae*. Cardano's principle of the reasoning on the mean has already been mentioned. It is clear from this that he is aware of the so-called *law of large numbers* in its most rudimentary form. Cardano's mathematics belongs to the period antedating the expression by means of formulas, so that he is not able to express the law explicitly in this way, but he uses it as follows:

when the probability for an event is p, then by a large number n of repetitions the number of times it will occur does not lie far from the value $m = np$.

In chapter thirty-two Cardano goes further toward the law of large numbers by determining what is called the *expectation of a probability variable* in some simple cases. Again he seems to imply from his argument on the mean, although there is no clear-cut statement to this effect, that when the play is repeated a large number of times, the arithmetic mean of the values obtained will be near this expectation.

He observes first that on a die or on a talus the various faces constitute the whole circuit and, therefore, if one divides the sum of the numbers by the number of faces, the result is their average or expectation.

On an astragal the values are 1, 3, 4, and 6 so that the average on one astragal is 3 1/2. In a throw of 4 of them the average will be 14. Cardano adds, and this is entirely his own speculation, that any throw with at least two aces is named a *dog* because, whatever the points on the two other astragals may be, the total sum cannot exceed the average point 14. He also determines correctly the average of the points by throws with three ordinary dice to be 10 1/2.

Most fascinating are the remarks which Cardano makes in the second section of the last chapter. He deals here with an example which at first seems very peculiar. He assumes that he has six dice of an unusual type. Each of them is marked on a single face only while the other five faces are blank. This marking is such that the first die carries an ace only, the second a deuce, and so on to the sixth die, which is stamped only with a six on one of its sides.

For one throw with these six dice Cardano computes the average result to be 3 1/2. To this he adds the following enigmatic comment: "However, the rule is not general, since in the case of most throws it will turn out less than three on account of the excess of the greater numbers which have to be computed. . . ."

It may seem strange that Cardano should have so much experience with this kind of dice that he can tell what will usually happen, but the explanation is in reality quite simple. The "blank" or "blind" dice were one of the favorite tools for cheating an unwary public at the kermisses. At this time and even much later one could see a long list of money prizes on the gambling booths at the country fairs, all to be awarded to the fortunate player who could throw a sufficiently high point on blind dice. The device could probably still flourish, because the conditions at first glance appear very attractive. The reasons for the deception may well have been a common topic of argument and wonder. Quite often the point zero was the only one on which the player lost his stake outright, while on points up to eight his money was returned to him. But for the high scores the prizes ran into good money, up to ninety times the stake for the highest point of twenty-one. Well-concealed to the average man was the fact that the probabilities for these large prizes, even by using fair dice, was near the vanishing point. For instance, for the point twenty-one one finds

$$p = \left(\tfrac{1}{6}\right)^6 = \tfrac{1}{46,656}$$

In this light Cardano's comments appear quite astute. Not only does he know that the mean point is 3.5 but he also realizes that such high points as 21 have pulled this mean upward so that to compensate for this there must be fewer cases above the mean than below the mean where the point values only run up to 3.

Cardano's probability studies for card games are not extensive and they all concern the game of primero. It was customary, as explained before, for one player, while he still had the privilege of drawing one or two cards, to propose an agreement or *fare a salvare* when the opponent had announced a high bid. Thus instead of taking his small chance he would agree to accept a modest but certain share of the stakes which was determined by fixed conventions and presumably stood in proportion to his likelihood of success in the draw.

25. Italian cards from Cardano's time.

According to Cardano it was usual in his circle that the pot be divided in two, one part to be played for and the other to be divided according to the rules of fare a salvare. He also suggests that such a division should either be compulsory and made in all cases when proposed or it should never be permitted. His argument is that the players might recognize the next card from the back and only accept the proposition if it were advantageous to him. It is evident that he was not accustomed to playing with decks in prime condition and marking of the cards was not rarely resorted to; Cardano observes that under such critical circumstances it might be better to agree to deal the bottom card.

Cardano mentions three cases in which it was customary to offer the fare a salvare, and toward the end of chapter sixteen he examines critically the rules of division.

In the first instance the high man has a three card flush with a relatively low point value, say 45, while the low man has only a two card flush but with a high point, for instance 36, that is, a five and a seven spot. In this case the second would win by drawing two cards if any one of them were in the suit of his flush. The stakes were then divided on an even basis.

The second case occurs when the high man has a three card flush, while his opponent cannot beat him on points even if he should succeed in obtaining a third card suitable to his other two. He then discards one card so that he has three cards in different suits and hopes for a primero on the draw, that is, a card in the fourth suit. The division would then be made at 2 to 1 in favor of the first.

In the third case, one player already has primero but the second has a three card flush. He discards the odd card and draws one card, hoping to obtain a full flush. Here the shares would be divided at 3 to 1.

Cardano analyzes these figures and comes to the conclusion that generally the rules favor the low man: "Therefore, I conclude that the scales are so balanced that we favor those who play with the more unfavorable fortune."

In the first case Cardano's statements are not very clear, but what he seems to want to say is that the equal division is advantageous to the player with a two card flush, for instance in hearts, because in drawing there are two hearts missing from the deck. No calculations are performed, but if one makes the natural supposition that there are eight hearts left among the remaining thirty-six cards, the probability for not obtaining a heart in two cards is

$$q = \frac{28.27}{36.35} = 0.6$$

so that the probability for winning is only $p = 0.4$. Cardano observes, however, that such an argument would not be appropriate if one knew from observing the discards that there remained a smaller or greater number of hearts than one should generally expect. He mentions the possibility that, toward the end, the deck would contain only ten cards of which five or even only one might be a heart. Such proportions would then have to be taken into account.

In the second case a player with three cards from different suits wants to obtain a primero by drawing a fourth card from the missing suit. Here Cardano first seems to report the commonly accepted view that, since there is one favorable suit out of four, the odds should be 3 to 1. However, toward the end of the chapter he returns to the question and states that the odds should be 5 to 2, corresponding to the probability

$$p = \frac{2}{7} = 0.286$$

for winning. To obtain this value Cardano must have reasoned correctly: there are thirty-six cards remaining and his own hand contains four cards outside the desired suit so that his probability of success is

$$p = \frac{10}{36} = 0.278$$

The slight discrepancy can easily be explained by Cardano's constant habit of rounding off the probabilities to simpler gambling odds "since in matters of this kind practical use alone should be regarded."

In the third and last instance the player has three cards in the same suit, say hearts, and wishes to draw another heart for a full flush. It is again evident that Cardano relies upon the proper reasoning: out of the ten hearts three are missing so that the probability of drawing a heart is

$$p = \frac{7}{36} = 0.194$$

Cardano does not state this fraction explicitly, but he vacillates between the odds 2 to 9, 1 to 5, and finally 1 to 4. The latter gives the probability

$$p = 0.200$$

which he accepts as being "nearer to the true reasoning."

This brings our examination of Cardano's probability theory to an end. It should have been made amply clear that his purpose was not only to resolve a special problem or two: it was also a systematic attempt to apply general principles to the rules in games and in this he was successful to a remarkable degree.

He seems to have analyzed the chances in all those game propositions where he believed that a mathematical approach was possible. He determined, as we have seen, the probabilities for all the various points on two and three dice, both for straight throws and for the throws as they were counted in backgammon. He gave the results for the combination of throws in arbitrary number. Not satisfied with dice, he took up theoretical questions of probabilities on four astragals as the games were played by the ancient Greeks and Romans. It is obvious that he could manage the chances for simple draws of cards as evidenced by his division rules in the game of primero. It must be added that almost all his results in these questions are correct with the exception of the systematic error in the table on backgammon which we have explained; later he perceived his error also on this point.

Cardano tackled the problem of the probable number of throws required to obtain a certain point on the dice, also called the problem of de Méré, but this was too complicated for him and his result does not go beyond a very rough gambler's approximation. But one of his most remarkable deductions is the correct formula for the repetition of a throw, two, three, or any number of times; this power law should most appropriately be called *Cardano's law*. Another noteworthy measure of Cardano's degree of understanding of the principles of probability is his discussion of the mean for dice throws, for astragals, and even for those cheating tools, the blind dice; there can be no doubt that he had a fairly good idea of the rule which is now called the law of large numbers.

All this was deduced and formulated more than a century before the correspondence between Pascal and Fermat in the year 1654 which is customarily considered as the discovery of probability theory. The only intervening document is a fragment by Galileo from about 1600, thus at least fifty years later than Cardano's studies; but Galileo deals only with chances on three dice and he shows in no way the scope and width of Cardano's work. *De Ludo Aleae* remained an unknown and buried manuscript which was not published until after the beginning steps had been taken over again by Pascal, Fermat, and Huygens. Thus it had no direct influence on the development of probability, yet in all fairness it should be observed as the first milestone in the long and very scenic road of probability from the past to its present dominating position in the mathematical and physical sciences.

Doubt has sometimes been expressed as to Cardano's genius and the originality of his work in mathematics. All of this is directly traceable to the charges which grew out of his controversy with Tartaglia, but even if one disregards entirely the piece of information which he admittedly received from his opponent, there remain ample achievements to secure his fame in algebra. But, for Cardano's probability studies in *De Ludo Aleae* there can be no detraction from his renown. We know of no previous work from which he could have gathered information. There is no indication that the discoveries and the spirit of penetration which one finds in Cardano's book can be credited to anybody but himself.

Bibliography

CHAPTER 1

Cardano, G. *Opera Omnia,* cura Caroli Sponii, 10 vols., Lyons. 1663.

Cardan, J. *The Book of My Life.* Translated from the Latin by Jean Stover, New York. 1930.

Bellini, A. "Gerolamo Cardano e il suo tempo." *Studii di Storia della Medicina,* vol. 8, Milan. 1947.

Dayre, J. "Jerome Cardan (1501-1576), Esquisse biographique." *Annales de l'Université de Grenoble.* Nouvelle série, vol. 4 (1927), pp. 245-355.

Eckman, J. "Jerome Cardan." Supplements to the *Bulletin of the History of Medicine,* no. 7 (1946).

Morley, H. *The Life of Girolamo Cardano of Milan, Physician,* 2 vols., London. 1854.

Waters, W. G. *Jerome Cardan, a biographical study,* London. 1898.

CHAPTER 2

Burr, C. W. "Jerome Cardan as Seen by an Alienist." *University of Pennsylvania, Public Lectures,* vol. 4 (1917), pp. 255-274.

Cardanus. *Comforte, translated into Englishe,* London. 1573.

Cass, M. M. *The first book of Jerome Cardan's "De Subtilitate,"* Bayard Press. 1934.

Dana, C. D. "The Story of a great Consultation: Jerome Cardan goes to Edinburgh." *Annals of Medical History,* vol. 3 (1921), pp. 122-135.

Lombroso, C. *Genio e follia in rapporta alla medicina legale, alla critica ed alla storia,* Turin. 1877.

Naudé, G. *Apologie pour les Grands Hommes soupçonnez de magie.* Amsterdam. 1712.

Rivari, E. *La mente di Girolamo Cardano,* Bologna. 1906.

Thorndike, Lynn. A *History of Magic and Experimental Science,* Columbia University Press. 1941.

CHAPTER 3

Bortolotti, E. "Italiani scopritori e promotori di teorie algebriche." *Annuario Università di Modena* (1918-1919), pp. 51-148.

Bortolotti, E. "I contributi del Tartaglia, del Ferrari, e della scuola matematica bolognese alla teoria algebrica delle equazioni cubiche." *Studie memorie per la storia dell'Università di Bologna,* vol. 9 (1926), pp. 57-108.

Bortolotti, E. "I cartelli di matematica disfida e la personalità psichica e morale di Girolamo Cardano." *Studie memorie per la storia dell'Università di Bologna*, vol. 12 (1935), pp. 3-79.

Cantor, M. *Vorlesungen über Geschichte der Mathematik*, Leipzig. 1880-1908.

Giordani, E. *I sei cartelli di matematica disfida di Lodovico Ferrari*, Milan. 1876.

Hall, V. "Life of Julius Caesar Scaliger (1484-1558)." *Transactions of the American Philosophical Society*, n.s. vol. 40, part 2.

Scaliger, J. C. *Exotericarum Exercitationum Libri XI. De Subtilitate ad Hieronymum Cardanum*, Frankfort. 1557.

Tartaglia, N. *Nuova scientia*, Venice. 1537.

Tartaglia, N. *Quesiti et inventioni diverse*, Venice. 1546.

Tartaglia, N. *Trattato generale di numeri e misure*, Venice. 1556-1560.

CHAPTER 4

La plus nouvelle Académie Universelle des Jeux; ou Divertissements innocens, Leyden. 1721.

Aretino, Pietro, *Le carte parlanti*, numerous editions.

Becq de Fouquières, L. *Les jeux des anciens*, 2nd ed., Paris. 1873.

Berni, Francesco. *Poesi e prose, criticamente curate da Ezio Chiorboli*, Florence. 1934.

Calcagnini, Celio. "De Talorum ac Tesserarum et Calculorum Ludis, ex more veterum." In J. Gronovius, *Thesaurus graecarum antiquitatum*, Leyden. 1697-1702.

CHAPTER 5

Cantor, M. *Vorlesungen über Geschichte der Mathematik*, 4 vols., Leipzig. 1880-1908.

Galilei, G. "Sopra le scoperte dei dadi." *Opere di Galileo Galilei*, edizione nationale, vol. 8, Florence. 1898.

Huygens, C. *De Ratiociniis in Ludo Aleae*, Amsterdam. 1657. French translation in Martinus Nijhoff, *Oeuvres complètes*, vol. 14, The Hague. 1920.

Montmort, R. de. *Essay d'Analyse sur les Jeux de Hazard*, Paris. 1708. Second augmented edition, 1713.

Todhunter, I. *A History of the Mathematical Theory of Probability from the time of Pascal to that of Laplace*, London, Macmillan Co. 1865. Reprint 1949, Chelsea Publishing Co., New York.

26. The wheel of fortune. From Gregor Reisch, *Margarita Philosophica* (1503).

Liber de Ludo Aleae

"THE BOOK ON GAMES OF CHANCE"

BY GEROLAMO CARDANO

•

TRANSLATED BY SYDNEY HENRY GOULD

NOTES BY OYSTEIN ORE

Contents

1 On kinds of games 185
2 On conditions of play 185
3 Who should play and when 186
4 The utility of play, and losses 188
5 Why I have dealt with gambling 189
6 The fundamental principle of gambling 189
7 The hanging dice box and dishonest dice 191
8 Conditions under which one should play 192
9 On the cast of one die 192
10 Why gambling was condemned by Aristotle 194
11 On the cast of two dice 195
12 On the cast of three dice 196
13 On composite numbers up to six and beyond and for two and three dice 197
14 On combined points 200
15 On an error which is made about this 202
16 On card games 206
17 On frauds in games of this kind 210
18 Customary conventions in primero 212
19 On the diversity of points or numbers in primero 213
20 On luck in play 215
21 On timidity in the throw 219
22 On the twofold division of games 220
23 On card games in which there is occasion for trained skill 220

24 On the difference between play with cards and play with dice 223
25 On card games 224
26 Do those who teach also play well? 225
27 Is there some element apart from skill which plays a role in the exercise of skill? 226
28 On far-reaching plans, judgment, and procedure [in Backgammon] 228
29 On the character of players 231
30 On games of chance among the ancients 232
31 On play with knucklebones 237
32 Conclusion of the work 240

1. On Kinds of Games

GAMES depend either on agility of body, as with a ball; or on strength, as with a discus and in wrestling; or on industriously acquired skill, as at chess; or on chance, as with dice and with knucklebones; or on both, as fritillus. Acquired ability may be of two kinds, as in games or in contests. Such a game is primero: for games of cards come under the same name[1] as games of dice, since in ancient times cards were unknown, and for that matter, even the material they are made from. Evidence of this is the fact that men wrote on parchment hides, as of kids for example, and on Egyptian papyrus, on tablets, on wax, and on linden bark. The game is called primero because it holds a primary place among the games of chance, either because of its beauty or because it consists of four primary associations (as it were) which is the number of primary elements[2] from which we (though not the whole world) are composed. Moreover, it has marvelous varieties.

2. On Conditions of Play

ATTENTION must be given to the state of the player and of his opponent, and also to the conditions under which the game is played, such as the amount of money wagered, the place, and the occasion; for the latter is of such importance that permission has been given for gambling at funeral banquets. Thus there is a heading in the law books, "Funeral expenses and games of chance." At other times it has been condemned by the law, as in the Titian and Cornelian Laws.

But in times of great anxiety and grief, it is considered to be not only allowable, but even beneficial. Also, it is per-

[1] The same name: *alea*.

[2] Aristotle's four elements: earth, fire, air, water. Cardano himself did not usually consider fire as an element.

mitted to men in prison, to those condemned to death, and to the sick, and therefore the law also permits it in times of grief. For certainly, if any occasion will justify it, none is so worthy of excuse as this one. In my own case, when it seemed to me after a long illness that death was close at hand, I found no little solace in playing constantly at dice.

However, there must be moderation in the amount of money involved; otherwise, it is certain that no one should ever play. As for the excuse made by some that it relieves boredom, this would be better done by pleasant reading, or by narrating tales or stories, or by one of the beautiful but not laborious arts. Among these latter, playing the lute or the virginals, or singing, or composing poetry will be more useful, and for three reasons. First, because such a change from serious business is more praiseworthy than gambling, either since something is produced, as in the case of painting, or because it is according to nature, as in music, or because the man learns something, as in reading or hearing tales or stories. Second, it is not without its element of toil and so does not rob us, against our will, of more time than it should. And time, as Seneca has rightly said in his work on *Length and Shortness of Life*, is the most precious of all things. Third, such employment of leisure is more respectable and does not present a bad example, as gambling does, particularly to one's children and servants. To these facts must be added that gambling arouses anger and disturbs the mind, and that sometimes a quarrel flares up over money, a thing which is disgraceful, dangerous, and prohibited by law. Finally, one cannot gamble alone, whereas the above delights can be enjoyed even when we are by ourselves.

3. Who Should Play and When

So, if a person be renowned for wisdom, or if he be old and dignified by a magistracy or any other civil honor or by a priesthood, it is all the worse for him to play; on the other hand, gambling is proportionately less of a reproach to boys, young men, and soldiers. The greater the amount of money involved, the greater the disgrace; *thus a certain holder of a very high priestly office* (*namely, a cardinal*) was severely blamed because he played after dinner with the Duke of Milan for a stake of five thousand crowns.

This fault is particularly detestable in princes and is defended by no one except courtiers and flatterers of the prince, who do it either from fear or because they receive gifts if the prince is lucky. In the meantime his subjects are despoiled and the poor are deprived of the aid which has been assigned to them and which is their due. If a man is victorious, he wastes the money won by gambling, whereas if he suffers defeat, then either he is reduced to poverty, when he is honest and without resources, or else to robbery, if he is powerful and dishonest, or again to the gallows, if he is poor and dishonest. One's opponent, too, if he is a man of ill repute or of low station in life who is devoted to the game, is a source of disgrace, and of loss also. For if you play assiduously with men of this kind, you will come away a confirmed gambler; or otherwise you will be the loser because of their greater experience, trickery, and skill.

Your opponent should be of suitable station in life; you should play rarely and for short periods, in a suitable place, for small stakes, and on suitable occasions, as at a holiday banquet. Your opponent might be the king, or a prelate of outstanding character,[3] or a relative by blood or by marriage. To play with professional gamblers is most disgraceful, and, as I have said, dangerous. The most respectable place is at home or at the house of a friend, where there can be no public scandal. Lawyers, doctors, and the like play at a disadvantage: for one thing, they appear to have too much leisure; for another, if they win, they seem

[3] Cardano made the acquaintance of the Duke of Milan at play and could count a number of cardinals among his good friends.

to be gamblers, and if they lose, perhaps they may be taken to be as unskilful in their own art as in gaming. Men of these professions incur the same judgment if they wish to practice music.

4. The Utility of Play, and Losses

As ADVANTAGES from well-managed play we obtain relaxation from anxiety and a pleasure from which we arise ready and eager for serious business; also knowledge of the character of our fellow-citizens for play is, as it were, a *rack* on which anger, greed, and honesty or dishonesty are made clear. For play both produces important evidence and is an actual torturer if the stakes are large. It is also a means of gaining friendship, and many have risen from obscurity because of the friendship of princes formed in play. This is what Cicero meant in his *Philippic* by the words "that fellow-player of yours, condemned for gambling."

But the losses incurred include lessening of reputation, especially if one has formerly enjoyed any considerable prestige; to this is added loss of time, vain words, including on occasion curses against the gods, the neglect of one's own business, the danger that it may become a settled habit, the time spent in planning after the game how one may recuperate, and in remembering how badly one has played. There are also disputes and often, which is worst of all, provocation to anger; for then a man is carried away into playing for high stakes and into feelings of enmity, so that he no longer has control of his own mind. As a result he throws out large sums of money and may be said to abandon them rather than play for them.

Play is a very good test of a man's patience or impatience. The greatest advantage in gambling comes from not playing at all. But there is very great utility in it as a test of patience, for a good man will refrain from anger even at the moment of rising from the game in defeat.

5. Why I Have Dealt with Gambling

There are two reasons why I have considered it fitting for me to deal with gambling: first, on account of its useful features, for, since it is useful, there must also be need for giving a systematic account of that usefulness under various conditions, and pointing out exactly how great it is. Even if gambling were altogether an evil, still, on account of the very large number of people who play, it would seem to be a natural evil. For that very reason it ought to be discussed by a medical doctor like one of the incurable diseases; for in every evil there is a least evil, in every disgrace a least disgrace, in every infamy a least infamy, and similarly in loss of time and fortune. Second, it has been the custom of philosophers to deal with the vices in order that advantage might be drawn from them, as, for example, in the case of anger. Thus it is not absurd for me to discuss gambling, not in order to praise it (for I have known some writers to attempt this, but their efforts are vain and form a bad example; I have read books of this kind) but in order to point out the advantages in it, and, of course, also its disadvantages, in order that the latter may be reduced to a minimum.

6. The Fundamental Principle of Gambling

The most fundamental principle of all in gambling is simply equal conditions, e.g. of opponents, of bystanders, of money, of situation, of the dice box, and of the die itself. To the extent to which you depart from that equality, if it is in your opponent's favor, you are a fool, and if in your own, you are unjust. With respect to your opponent, if he is more powerful than you, or unscrupulous, or likely to be violent, or a man who hopes to win everything by creating sufficient delay, if he is given to complaint or litigation, or is clamorous, or deceitful, if he can disturb your equanimity by making you afraid or angry, then he is the worst man in the world for you; and to play with him is not to play but simply to lose your money.

And there is even greater danger to be feared from kibitzers, if they favor your opponent; and so it happens that, if you play in a large crowd of people, you can scarcely avoid folly if they are against you, or else injustice if they are for you. They can injure you in many ways: for example, by giving your opponent open advice and information, which is a twofold evil, since it not only helps their side but also provokes you to anger and disturbs you; for an angry man, as long as he is angry, is simply insane. Others will annoy you by their disorderly talk, even without giving definite information. Some will purposely consult you on serious business; some will even be so impudent as to provoke you to anger by quarreling with you; others will make fun of you in order to make you angry; others, more modest than these, will indicate to your opponent by foot or by hand that the decision he has made is not the right one; others again, a little farther off, will do this with a nod, perhaps with no other purpose, it may be, than to help him by filling your mind with suspicion. Still others will state falsely how the die has fallen; others again will worry you by accusing *you* of such things.

For all these reasons it is of the very greatest advantage to you to have your own supporters if you wish to win unjustly; and to play otherwise in the presence of a crowd is simply to waste your money, not to contend for it; for even if no trickery takes place, suspicion itself disturbs a man and makes him err, so that a suspicious man should not play. There is the same danger when your opponent seizes the die very quickly or moves his counters in such a way that you cannot see what he is doing or what the die has shown; and similarly if he plays with coins which are counterfeit, or debased, or excessively worn by water; or if the situation is one to cause fear, or if you are in a place of ill repute; and if the die is dishonest or if you are playing with a hanging dice box.[4]

7. The Hanging Dice Box and Dishonest Dice

SET the round gaming boards in the middle; if they incline toward your opponent, then the dice box will incline in the opposite direction, and this is unfavorable to you. Similarly, if there is a slope toward you, then the box will be out of plumb in your favor; but if the dice box is not moved, then this does not matter. Similarly, if the board catches the light from the side opposite to you, then this is bad, since it disturbs your mind; on the other hand, it is to your advantage to have the board against a dark background. Again, they say it is of benefit to take up your position facing a rapidly rising moon.

As for the die itself, there are two sorts of danger. In the first place, every die, even if it is an acceptable one, has its favored side either because of its shape, or for some other reason, or by mere chance; and if in this way a large point is changed into a small one, or vice versa, you can readily understand how much of a difference it makes. In the second place, the die may be dishonest either because it has been rounded off, or because it is too narrow (a fault which is plainly visible), or because it has been extended in one direction by pressure on opposite faces. Consequently, it should receive a threefold testing, since there are three pairs of opposite faces which determine the surface to show uppermost. So these matters must be considered very carefully. There are even worse ways of being cheated at cards; these will be noted later on. In everything one must keep a watchful eye and take note of any disparity among the cards.

[4] It is not clear whether the word fritillus here should be translated as dice box or gaming board. See also p. 111.

8. Conditions Under Which One Should Play

It is foolish to play even for small stakes for the mere purpose of being beaten because you do not notice what is going on; but it is also foolish to devote yourself entirely to gambling in order that you may win; for it is inevitable that he who plays more rarely should be less skilful. But should you therefore abandon all study of the arts in order that you may win at dice? And this only for small gain or even with the sole result of losing, and being angry at yourself and an object of scorn to others? And if you should lose a large amount, then certainly the gain to the victor is not so great as the loss to the loser; for usually he gives away a great deal; the man is wasteful and his time is lost; and when the die once falls unluckily for him, his loss may be greater than the net gain of many wins.

So you ought to be more skilful than your opponent, and more experienced, or else you ought to play in such a way that it does not matter how the die falls, as will be the case if you play for small stakes or with your loved ones for a short time after dinner. But if you are determined to play for large stakes, then play constantly with an opponent who is neither more experienced than yourself nor more fortunate, and let the conditions not be unlucky for you. For luck plays a very large part in these matters also.

9. On the Cast of One Die

The talus has four faces, and thus also four points. But the die has six; in six casts each point should turn up once; but since some will be repeated, it follows that others will not turn up. The talus is represented as having flat surfaces, on each one of which it lies on its back; it can be seen in this way and is therefore so depicted; in actual practice, however, it is not so, but boys spin it as though it were a spindle and it does not have the form of a die.[5]

One-half of the total number of faces always represents equality;[6] thus the chances are equal that a given point will

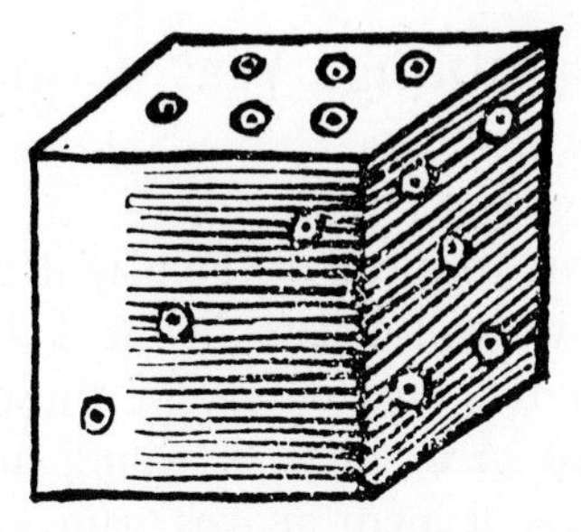

27. Tessera. From Frisius, *Arithmeticae Practicae* (1553).

turn up in three throws, for the total circuit is completed in six, or again that one of three given points will turn up in one throw. For example, I can as easily throw one,

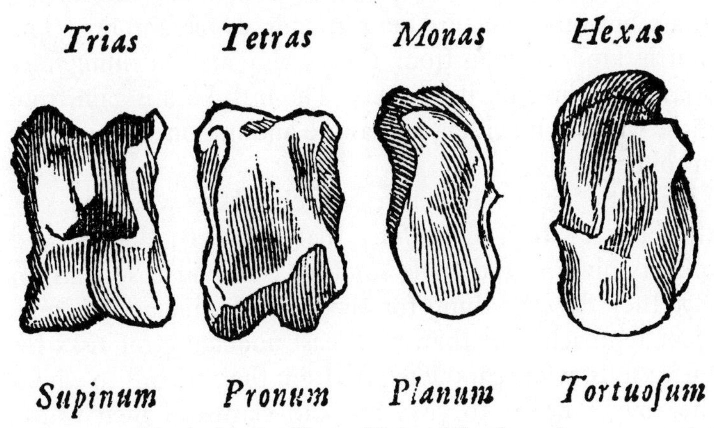

28. Astragals. From Hyde, *Mandragorias.*

three, or five as two, four, or six. The wagers are therefore laid in accordance with this equality if the die is honest,

[5] The missing illustrations have been replaced from other sources.
[6] See explanation on p. 149.

and if not they are made so much the larger or smaller in proportion to the departure from true equality. But (as I have said) these facts contribute a great deal to understanding but hardly anything to practical play.[7]

10. Why Gambling Was Condemned by Aristotle

But when we come to speak of the play itself and of actual gambling, which we will discuss below, I do not hold anyone blameless in this matter except those who play for money because of great grief of mind; and gambling is disgraceful because a man makes gain from his friend against that friend's will. For the case stands thus: gain from those who are both willing and aware is best; next best, is gain from those who are aware and unwilling. To the first class belong lawyers and doctors, and to the second merchants. The third kind is gain from those who, being aware but unwilling, are one's friends, as in gambling. The fourth kind is gain from those who are unwilling and unaware, as in gain by trickery. The fifth kind is gain from those who are unwilling and aware and not one's friends, as in robbery.

Aristotle gives another reason elsewhere when he says (4. *Ethics*, Chap. 1, *in fin.*) that gamblers, thieves, and robbers ply a sordid trade for they traffic in base gain; in fact they do everything for the sake of gain and thereby incur reproach. But thieves at least undergo great risks for their spoils, while gamblers gain from their friends to whom they ought rather to give. So both classes of men whose aim is to make gain where they ought not, traffic in base gain, and all such acquisitive acts are sordid. Moreover, a confirmed gambler is a perjurer and a blasphemer, and is at the same time prodigal and greedy; and if not so already

[7] The meaning is that no dice games were played with only one die.

by nature, he soon becomes irascible; he cherishes vain hopes in his idleness and he corrupts the youth.

Now the Christians tolerate gambling, though it was condemned by the ancients; but they do not allow cursing, and so they prosecute the lesser evils. As for the fact that this evil takes its rise among princes, they, of course, wish to allow themselves everything; and so, as I have said, gambling is a very great evil in the state. Nevertheless, in times of great fear and sorrow, when even the greatest minds are much disturbed, gambling is far more efficacious in counteracting anxiety than a game like chess, since there is the continual expectation of what fortune will bring. Nor does it claim a man's whole attention as strictly as chess does. At such a time physical games are harmful and dangerous.

11. On the Cast of Two Dice

In the case of two dice, there are six throws with like faces, and fifteen combinations with unlike faces, which when doubled gives thirty, so that there are thirty-six throws in all, and half of all these possible results is eighteen. As for the throws with unlike faces, they occur in pairs in the eighteen casts of equality, so that equality for such a throw consists of nine casts; and this reasoning gives eighteen casts for equality for a throw (1,1); for in that number of casts this throw can appear and not appear with equal probability; and similarly for the throws (2,2) and (3,3).

But the throw (1,2) can turn up in two ways, so that for it there is equality in nine casts; and if it turns up more frequently or more rarely, that is a matter of luck.

The number of throws containing at least one ace is eleven out of the circuit of thirty-six; or somewhat more than half of equality; and in two casts of two dice the number of ways of getting at least one ace twice is more than 1/6 but less than 1/4 of equality.

In three casts of two dice the number of times that at least one ace will turn up three times in a row falls far short of the whole circuit, but its turning up twice differs from equality by about 1/12. The argument is based upon the fact that such a succession is in conformity with a series of trials and would be inaccurate apart from such a series.

Moreover, a repeated succession, such as favorable points occurring twice, arises from circuits performed in turn; for example, in 3,600 casts, the equality is 1/2 of that number, namely, 1,800 casts; for in such a number of casts the desired result may or may not happen with equal probability. So the whole set of circuits is not inaccurate, except insofar as there can be repetition, even twice or three times, in one of them. Accordingly, this knowledge is based on conjecture which yields only an approximation, and the reckoning is not exact in these details; yet it happens in the case of many circuits that the matter falls out very close to conjecture.

12. On the Cast of Three Dice

Throws with three alike are the same, except in one respect, as the throws with two alike in the preceding chapter; thus there are 6 of them. The number of different throws of three dice with doublets and one different point is 30, and each of these occurs in 3 ways, which makes 90. Again, the number of different throws with three different faces is 20, each of which occurs in 6 ways, which makes 120. Thus the circuit of all of them will be 216 and equality will be 108.

I shall set down, by way of example, some simple terms, together with the number of various ways in which they can occur. With respect to these simple terms, then, in the case of a doublet and one different, there are 6 possible values for the like faces and 5 for the odd point; so, since there are 6 faces, there will be 30 varieties of throws.

Also, each of them can be varied in three ways, making 90. But the 20 cases with three unlike faces, since each of them can be varied in 6 ways, will make 120. Thus a triplet throw is the 1/108 part of equality, while any doublet and one different point, since it can be varied in 3 ways, will be the 1/36 part of equality. This is just as in the case of two dice where a doublet is 1/18 of equality, and so occurs once in 18 throws, which is 1/6 of 108. Therefore, in comparison with the former, it will occur three times as often.

Such, then, is the law for doublets, as we shall say, or for the calculation of the stake in this case. But two distinct faces, as (1,2), we shall distinguish thus: that, if an ace is adjoined, it will be done in three ways, and if a deuce, then in the same number of ways, therefore already 6. Moreover, it happens in 4 other ways: but the latter are varied, each one, in 6 different ways; therefore there will be 24, so that with the remaining 6 there will be 30.

But 35 to 36 has the proportion of equality to 108 when compared to 12, therefore almost 1/6 but not quite.

But three different faces, as (1,2,3), bear to the number of equality exactly the same proportion as in doublets for two dice. Moreover, the single faces themselves in one die have a proportion 1/3 of equality; since, therefore, there are three dice, they will obtain the proportion of equality, so that out of the 216 possible results, each single face will be found in 108 and will not be found in as many. The reasoning is exactly the same for one face in the case of two dice; the latter is equal to the whole circuit in three throws and to equality in half that number.

13. On Composite Numbers Up to Six and Beyond and for Two and Three Dice

IN THE CASE of two dice, the points 12 and 11 can be obtained respectively as (6,6) and as (6,5). The point 10 consists of (5,5) and of (6,4), but the latter can occur in two ways, so that the whole number of ways of obtaining 10 will be 1/12 of the circuit and 1/6 of equality. Again, in the case of 9, there are (5,4) and (6,3), so that it will be 1/9 of the circuit and 2/9 of equality. The 8 point consists of (4,4), (3,5), and (6,2). All 5 possibilities are thus about 1/7 of the circuit and 2/7 of equality. The point 7 consists of (6,1), (5,2), and (4,3). Therefore the number of ways of getting 7 is 6 in all, 1/3 of equality and 1/6 of the circuit. The point 6 is like 8, 5 like 9, 4 like 10, 3 like 11, and 2 like 12.

In the game Fritillus 11 cases are to be added, because the number can be shown on a single die. Thus, the point 2 is obtained in 12 different ways, which is 2/3 of equality and 1/3 of the circuit. The point 3 is obtained in 13 different ways, 4 in 14, 5 in 15, which is 10/12 of equality and 5/12 of the whole circuit, and 6 in 16, which is very close to equality.

TABLES FOR CASTS WITH TWO AND THREE DICE

Sors with two dice

2,12 : 1	3,11 : 2	4,10 : 3	Equality by 18
5, 9 : 4	6, 8 : 5	7 : 6	

Sors and Fritillus with three dice

Sors	*Fritillus*	
3,18 : 1	3 : 115	
4,17 : 3	4 : 120	
5,16 : 6	5 : 126	
6,15 : 10	6 : 133	Circuit 216
7,14 : 15	7 : 33	Equality 108
8,13 : 21	8 : 36	
9,12 : 25	9 : 37	
10,11 : 27	10 : 36	
	11 : 33	
	12 : 26	

Remaining points as in Sors

13 : 21
14 : 15

. . . .

Single point has 108 cases
Two points have 111 cases

In the case of three dice there will be three faces. The point 3 exceeds equality in Fritillus, in Sors it is represented only by 3 aces, that is, by 1/108 of equality. In Fritillus the point 4 can be obtained in 120 ways; in Sors it is 1/36 of equality, or 1/72 of the circuit. The point 5 arises from a double ace or a double deuce; it will therefore be 1/18 of equality in Sors; but in Fritillus, it can be obtained in 126 ways, that is, more than equality by 1/6. The point 6, however, in Sors can be obtained in 10 ways, namely, 3 deuces, 2 aces with a 4, and (3,2,1). So in Fritillus there will be these same possibilities and in addition those which are made with two dice, namely (3,3), (1,5), and (4,2); these are 15 and with the 10 others they become 25, so that there are 133. The point 7 can be obtained in Sors in 15 ways; in Fritillus it already ceases to be the half or to have equality. Therefore, there are only these same possibilities and those which are produced by two dice, and there are (1,6), (2,5), and (4,3); therefore they are 18. The sum is 33, less than a third of equality. But the point 8 in Sors occurs in 21 ways; in Fritillus it is 1/3 of equality, namely 36. The point 9 in Sors occurs in 25 ways, and in Fritillus in 12 more, therefore 37 in all. The point 10 in Sors occurs in 27 ways and in Fritillus in 9 more, consequently 36; the other numbers correspond in turn in Sors, as you see in the table. But in Fritillus the point 11 occurs in only 33 ways and 12 in 26. The rest of the numbers above 12 are equal to those which are in Sors.

14. On Combined Points

We must enter upon a consideration of this sort in the case of two dice, because the ace occurs in 11 casts, and the deuce likewise, and the trey and so on for each of them, but the ace or deuce do not occur in 22 casts but only in 20. For the ace occurs in 11 and the deuce in 9 more. Thus, if the trey is added, there will not be 29, nor 31, but 27, and in general numbers of casts are those given in the table. Thus, if all the casts are collected, there are 36; for since this is the complete circuit, it is necessary that in every throw some face should occur because they complete the number of the circuit.

TWO DICE		TOTAL
Cases for 1 *point*	11	11
Additional for: 2	9	20
3	7	27
4	5	32
5	3	35
6	1	36

If, therefore, someone should say, "I want an ace, a deuce, or a trey," you know that there are 27 favorable throws, and since the circuit is 36, the rest of the throws in which these points will not turn up will be 9; the odds will therefore be 3 to 1. Therefore in 4 throws, if fortune be equal, an ace, deuce, or trey will turn up 3 times and only one throw will be without any of them; if, therefore, the player who wants an ace, deuce, or trey were to wager three ducats and the other player one, then the former would win three times and would gain three ducats; and the other once and would win three ducats; therefore in the circuit of 4 throws they would always be equal. So this is the rationale of contending on equal terms; if, therefore, one of them were to wager more, he would strive under an unfair condition and with loss; but if less, then with gain. Similarly, if the 4 be included, there will be 32 favorable throws, and the number of remaining throws will be only 4. Therefore, the player will place a stake eight times as great as his opponent, because the proportion 32 to 4 is eightfold, and similarly for the other cases, nor is there any need for an argument based on the average.

Consequently, we can make the corresponding statements in the other cases. Thus if we want (1,1) or (2,2), there are 2 favorable throws; and since there are 34 other throws, the odds are 17 to 1. Thus, also, if we want a (1,1), the odds are 35 to 1, and in fact all the above rules ought to be reduced to this one principle, as can be discerned from the equality of the wagers. For example, in order that an ace may turn up, since there are 11 favorable throws, the odds will be 25 to 11, a little more than 2 to 1.

The same reasoning is to be observed in the case of three dice, both for simple and for combined faces, and let us state, from the above, that there are 108 casts of the ace (Chap. 12 in fine). Therefore, it will be necessary to find 6 terms, of which the largest shall be 108, and the rest shall be equidistant from this number and from each other, and such that all together they make up 216, as you see in the table:

THREE DICE		DIFFERENCE
Cases for 1 *point*	91	30
Additional for: 2	61	24
3	37	18
4	19	12
5	7	6
6	1	
	216	

For the ace does not have a number of favorable throws equal to half the whole circuit, but the odds are 91 to 125, or very nearly, if inverted, 25 to 18, greater therefore than 4 to 3. So the player who has wagered that an ace will not turn up will gain to the extent to which in 7 turns he has his throw free of it, and if he wagers 4, he will still gain those 3. In the same way we must enter upon the consideration in the remaining cases. It is evident that with two dice the increments are equal. But for three they have an equal excess, as is clear from the table.

Other questions must be considered more subtly, since mathematicians also may be deceived, but in a different way. I have wished this matter not to lie hidden because many people, not understanding Aristotle, have been deceived, and with loss. So there is one general rule, namely, that we should consider the whole circuit, and the number of those casts which represents in how many ways the favorable result can occur, and compare that number to the remainder of the circuit, and according to that proportion should the mutual wagers be laid so that one may contend on equal terms.

But if two casts are necessary, we shall multiply them in turn, and the remainders for those numbers in turn, and if three are necessary, or four, we shall do the same, and then we shall have to make the comparison in accordance with the numbers thus obtained. Thus, if it is necessary for someone that he should throw an ace twice, then you know that the throws favorable for it are 91 in number, and the remainder is 125; so we multiply each of these numbers by itself and get 8,281 and 15,625, and the odds are about 2 to 1. Thus, if he should wager double, he will contend under an unfair condition, although in the opinion of some the condition of the one offering double stakes would be better. In three successive casts, therefore, if an ace is necessary, the odds will be 753,571 to 1,953,125, or very nearly 5 to 2, but somewhat greater.

15. On an Error Which Is Made About This

But this reasoning seems to be false, even in the case of equality, as, for example, the chance of getting one of any three chosen faces in one cast of one die is equal to the chance of getting one of the other three, but according to this reasoning there would be an even chance of getting a chosen face each time in two casts, and thus in three, and four, which is most absurd. For if a player with two dice can with equal chances throw an even and an odd number, it does not follow that he can with equal fortune throw an even number in each of three successive casts.

But when he produces an odd number on the first cast or on the second or third cast in one trial, he can be deceived in his reckoning by the eight various results. Therefore, in comparisons where the probability is one-half, as of even faces with odd, we shall multiply the number of casts by itself and subtract one from the product, and the proportion which the remainder bears to unity will be the proportion of the wagers to be staked. Thus, in 2 successive casts we shall multiply 2 by itself, which will be 4; we shall subtract 1; the remainder is 3; therefore a player will rightly wager 3 against 1; for if he is striving for odd and throws even, that is, if after an even he throws either even or odd, he is beaten, or if after an odd, an even. Thus he loses three times and wins once.

And for 3 successive casts we shall multiply 3 by itself; the result is 9; take away one; the remainder is 8. The proportion of 8 to 1 is valid for 3 successive casts, and for 4 casts this proportion is 15 to 1, and for five, 24 to 1. Thus, in 125 casts, there will be only five sequences of throws in their proper places, that is, with the same number of consecutive even throws, so that they may begin with an odd number either in the first or the sixth or the eleventh place. For otherwise there would be more than five consecutive even throws. All this reasoning can be demonstrated from the number of places in each of the circuits mentioned, although in the cases involving multiplication it seems to be false. For example, if we consider the number 20, the odds become 7,999 to 1. Yet it can scarcely be believed that in 7,999 throws a player can cast an even number twenty times in a row. But we have demonstrated this; because, although in 8,000 performed only once, this reasoning can deceive us, still in an infinite number of throws, it is almost necessary for it to happen; for the magnitude of the circuit is the length of time which shows forth all forms.

We turn now to cases where the probability is not 1/2; for example, in the above-mentioned case where we want an ace, deuce, or trey on either of two dice, the odds are 3 to 1. In order to make the study easier, we shall consider one die only. We therefore take a talus with four faces, having an even number on one face and an odd number on the other three, and we investigate the wagers for successive appearances of an odd face. Let us give to the odd faces the names *a*, *b*, and *c* and to the even one *d*, and in the following investigation let there be 4 columns, as you see in the table.

A	B	C	D
a	a	a	a
b	b	b	b
c	c	c	c
d	d	d	d

Let the first column be written under *A* and the second under *B* and let the second cast be combined with the first so that there will be 16, of which 9 will be odd on both faces and the other 7 will contain an even face.

Similarly, for a die with 3 faces, 2 of them being odd, there will be only 4 odd results and the other 5 will be even, and if there are 5 faces and 4 of them are odd, there will be 16 odd results out of the 25 possibilities, and the other 9 will be even.

In all these cases the whole number is multiplied into itself and similarly the number of similar faces into itself, and the latter number is compared to the remainder, and similarly, if there are only 3 faces and 2 of them are favorable to us, we shall multiply the whole number into itself, and then that number into itself, and this part will be compared to the remainder. Thus, in the case of one die, let the ace and the deuce be favorable to us; we shall multiply 6, the number of faces, into itself: the result is 36; and two multiplied into itself will be 4; therefore the odds are 4 to 32, or, when inverted, 8 to 1.

If three throws are necessary, we shall multiply 3 times; thus, 6 multiplied into itself and then again into itself gives 216; and 2 multiplied into itself and again into 2, gives 8; take away 8 from 216: the result will be 208; and so the odds are 208 to 8, or 26 to 1. And if four throws are necessary, the numbers will be found by the same reasoning, as you see in the table; and if one of them be subtracted from the other, the odds are found to be 80 to 1.

All this is for one die only, but the same reasoning holds for two and three dice also, as we shall show by an example. Let the favorable cases be the ace, deuce, or trey, occurring in three successive casts. As already mentioned, the number of the circuit is 36 and the number of favorable throws is 27. We multiply 36 into itself 3 times; the result is 46,656. Multiply 27 into itself 3 times; the result will be 19,683. Subtract the smaller from the larger; the remainder will be 26,973, which gives the odds when compared to 19,683. These odds, namely, the ratio of the remainder to the smaller number, are greater than 4 to 3 and less than 3 to 2.

Similarly, it has been stated that with three dice any one face, whichever one it may be, has, taken by itself, 91 favorable cases in the whole circuit of 216. Therefore, if that face is required three times in a row, we shall multiply the whole circuit, and the result is 9,324,125. When the latter number is divided by the smaller of the above numbers, namely, 753,571, we get the odds determining the stake to be wagered, namely, a little greater than 12 to 1.

From this it is clear that any other reasoning is not satisfactory, but that this reasoning is generally true.

16. On Card Games

If I should wish to speak about all of them, it would be an endless task, but there are two kinds, those with planning and those without such planning. There is a difference from play with dice, because the latter is open, whereas play with cards takes place from ambush, for they are hidden.

Primero is the noblest of all. It consists of four cards as far as difference of kind is concerned: for among the French, Spanish, Germans, and Italians cards are of four different suits; there are thirteen cards of each suit and so fifty-two in all. They run from one to ten in the sequence of numbers. Then there is the king together with the jack, and the French have a queen and the Italians a knight.

In primero the cards eight, nine, and ten are removed: the king, the jack, and the queen or knight are each worth 10. From the two to the five, 10 is added, so that they are worth 12, 13, 14, and 15; and the six and the seven are tripled, so that the six is worth 18 and the seven 21, while the ace is worth 16. So the greatest total (on three cards of the same suit) consists of the seven, the six, and the ace, and they are 21, 18, and 16 or 55 in all. But if the number of these cards is completed by adding the five, then all these cards of the same suit make up the number 70.

Now there are two kinds of primero. In one the greater number wins, and this number is different according to the nature of the hands; in the other the smaller number wins; and in this latter kind, which is very little in use, the smallest number to be obtained on cards of various suits is 20, while in primero it is 40 and in fluxus 42. But the hands are the same as in the former kind and keep the same order relative to one another.

There are five kinds of bids: numerus, primero, supremus, fluxus, and chorus.

Numerus occurs when two or three cards are of the same suit. The least possible result here is 20, which is made from two minor cards, which they call face cards because they have depicted on them the human face (as one says) of the king, the queen (or the knight, as the case may be), and the jack. The greatest numerus is 54: it consists of three cards, the seven, the six, and the five.

The second type of hand is *primero*, when all the cards are of different suits, and, whatever it may be, it surpasses every numerus. In it the least number is 40 (as I have said), and the greatest is 81.

This primero, however great, is surpassed by *supremus*, i.e. 55, when three cards of the same suit are seven, six, and one, which make up 55.

In the fourth place is *fluxus*, which consists of four cards of the same suit and surpasses primero and supremus. Here the smallest number (as I have said) is 42 and the greatest is 70.

The fifth type of hand is like primero but has all its cards of the same denomination, as four sixes or sevens, or four kings. But three kings and one queen do not make a *chorus*, although all are valued at the same number, namely, 10. This hand surpasses all the preceding ones. In it the greatest number wins and this greatest number is 84. If the face cards are equal, as four kings and four jacks, the four kings do not win, since they are not superior in value, but that player who is nearest to the dealer on the right. This is the general rule for all equal numbers in equal bids.

The cards are dealt around twice, two at a time and not singly. It is not permissible to count diverse bids as more than the greatest of these, but supremus can be considered as primero when another has bid primero. Also chorus can always be concealed for primero and for fluxus when another has announced it.

But there is one evil custom which ought to be condemned: some players show chorus, then cast away a card at a certain moment and later receive cards in exchange and wish to remain with chorus, but this procedure is too contentious and offers occasion for fraud in many ways. For that reason, luck ought to be enjoyed as it comes; for if it had wished to favor the player in the exchange of cards, it would not have shown itself in the matter beforehand. This rule ought not to be disregarded.

There are three cases in which one customarily calls for new cards:

First when you have the lower point, for instance, your opponent has 45 and you have 36, so that with any card among the two [in your suit] you will be the winner.

Secondly, if your opponent should have the point 40 but you have three cards of different suits, then you will only be able to win by primero.

Thirdly, if he should have primero, or the supreme point, or even only a higher point but in such a way that your three cards have a lower value, then it will be necessary for you to complete a fluxus in order to win.

It is customary to remove a part of each pot, namely, one-half or thereabouts, and the remainder is left to chance in order that it may belong to the victor.

By such reasoning the sharing in the first case will be made on an equal basis (unless from the discarded cards one knows that there remain fewer or more than one should expect in general: for if ten cards should remain to be distributed, and in these there remain five, or only one, one would have to argue differently). In the primero the share ought to be one-half to twice, and in fluxus one-third to three times.

But I shall tell what should be done rather than what is done since the customs vary in different countries. Thus, in order that the conditions should be fair, the amount removed should be divided as follows:

In the first case according to the amount by which this equality is preferable to the one already holding two cards; for the two other cards occupy two different suits, but the four cards should be so that an encounter occurs. But if there is some more subtle reasoning, it is now fitting to pass over it, since in matters of this kind practical use alone should be regarded.

But in the second case one player has already received two shares, the other player one, as we said. Out of four turns he would lose in three cases and win only in one so that in one circuit he would lose all, which is therefore the condition. But players are moved by the reasoning that, if two cards were awaited, it would be suitable to take equal shares, therefore out of half of two cards, half of the share. It is necessary to take up the reasoning as follows: out of four cases in one circuit he would lose three and win one, so that he would lose half of that which he has. Therefore he will necessarily lose half of his stake while the opponent gains as much. Thus he should receive only 1/4 of the removed part and the opponent 3/4.

But in fluxus, since there are three cards lacking from that suit among those to be dealt, it is necessary to withdraw five shares of which the one of the two who has three cards wins one; rather, he will receive only two and his fellow player nine.

Holding one card to primero is preferable on the basis of the 1/3 share we already mentioned. Therefore, I conclude that the scales are so balanced that we favor those who play with the more unfavorable fortune.

In the case of primero, the one who expects it should accept two shares, the other five. But in the case of fluxus he should have one to the other's five shares, or rather one share to the other's four and this is nearer to the true reasoning.

However, care must be taken that this is not done arbitrarily, but either always or never, for otherwise you will play under most unfavorable conditions. For the opponent may be able to recognize the card from the outside and so, if it should be favorable to you or to him, he may not accept the proposal; and he will by no means do so if it should be favorable to you and not to him. But if it is required to accept the conditions, let it be done before the card is requested since then the cards are drawn from below and not from the top.

17. On Frauds in Games of This Kind

CARDS have this in common with dice, that what is desired may be got by fraud: the most contemptible kind is that which is backed up by the sword; a second kind has to do with recognition of the cards—in its worst form it consists of using marked cards, and in another form it is more excusable, namely, when the cards are put in a special order and it is necessary to remember this order. Such players are accustomed, when they know where the desired card is, to keep it on the bottom and to deal out others, which chance alone would not call for, until they get the suppressed card for themselves. But the other players in the first-mentioned class carry out very dangerous frauds which are worthy of death, as in fact the latter is also, but it is more concealed. Those, however, who know merely by close attention what cards they are to expect are not usually called cheats, but are reckoned to be prudent men.

As for those who use marked cards, some mark them at the bottom, some at the top, and some at the sides. The first kind are marked quite close to the bottom and may be either rough or smooth or hard; the second are marked with color and with slight imprints with a knife; while on the edges cards can be marked with a figure, a rough spot, with interwoven knots or humps, or with grooves hollowed out with a file. Some players examine the appearance of a card by means of mirrors placed in their rings. I omit the devices of kibitzers—the organum, the consensus, and the like.[8]

Certainly, in view of the small amount of pleasure provided by gambling and the rarity with which it favors our wishes, there are so many difficulties in it, and so many possibilities of loss, that really there is nothing better than not to play at all. There are also some who smear the cards with soap so that they may slide easily and slip past one another. This was the trick practiced upon me by the well-known Thomas Lezius of Venice,[9] patrician, when in my youth I was addicted to gambling.

Now, in general, gambling is nothing but fraud and number and luck. Against fraud the one remedy is to beware of men of deceitful mind; for, just as a good man cannot be a cheat, so a cheat cannot be a good man. When you suspect fraud, play for small stakes, have spectators, shuffle the cards instead of merely collecting them, and if another collects them without shuffling, he is acting fraudulently. Have your own cards, and if others send out to buy cards, let them buy from men you can trust. Examine them inside and out and edgewise; touch the corners; if they are rough, or too smooth, or hard, or uneven, do not play; for before you can recognize what is wrong, your opponents will perhaps ruin you. Finally, let no one examine the cards in private. In primaria (which is also called primero), it is customary to uncover the cards from the back and from above as little as possible so that the kibitzers cannot see anything; a great part of the art appears to consist in this, and players boast about their skill in this respect.

Considerable perplexity arises on the following point.

[8] The "organ" was a loose floor board under the table on which one player rested his foot, receiving signals from an accomplice who moved the board slightly, usually by pulling a string from another room. The "consensus" is an unknown device; the word itself means complicity or collusion.

[9] Thomas Lezius was probably one of Cardano's gambling companions during the time he lived in the town of Sacco.

Since prestidigitators are capable of such admirable feats, why is it that they are usually unlucky at cards? It would seem reasonable that, just as they are able to deceive us with balls, pots, and coins, they should also be able to do it with cards and so invariably come out winners. But the condemned Spaniard was ordered (in fact, the prohibition, they say, was on pain of death) not to play, seeing that he could at will produce four cards that make chorus[10] either by deceiving the eye or by making the exchange by quickness of hand; for we must assign to either of these a prodigious art of prestidigitation. But Franciscus Sorna of Naples[11] (about whom I have spoken elsewhere, at the beginning of book 18, *De Subtilitate*) could change cards so quickly that nothing more wonderful could be imagined.

18. Customary Conventions in Primero

IN PRIMERO certain conventions are considered customary. It is not permitted to draw from the discards: that is considered a fraud. Additions are therefore made gradually from the deck. If the point is simple, or even if it is superior, they change cards once. If primero or fluxus is present when a player has divulged his hand, then that player is master of the lot.

Those who admit four of a kind, or in other words chorus, do not admit the supremus in order that the pot may be increased, and those who admit the supremus do not admit chorus in order that it may be permissible to increase the stake. He who, not having announced his primero or fluxus, shall have increased the deposit, except when purposely changing cards, loses his deposit; but if he has not increased it, he is compelled at the will of the others to change cards; if one has too little and the others more, then those

[10] Chorus: four of a kind.

[11] In chapter eighteen of *De Subtilitate* the man's name is given as Soma. For his card tricks see p. 133.

who so wish can contend separately beyond that which is least. And even though that third player should win, still they contend for the remainder just as if they were playing alone among themselves.

If anyone places a wager from the beginning, then if someone accepts it, the others are absolved. If no one does, then the last player from him who places is compelled to stake. If he wishes to bet more than the first amount, anyone who wishes may accept the condition, or else refuse it, but for the first bet (as I have said) the last player is held responsible. If no one bets, they are compelled to exchange one or two cards according to their judgment. There are those who play for equal stakes in the case of two cards and the game is a mixture, at least according to my opinion, of the French Geleus and primero.

If anyone wins with the greater point, he is compelled to show another card. If he does not do so, he loses his deposit because he could have fluxus. If he professes to have primero and his fellow-player refuses to increase the deposit, he is compelled to show primero. For he might have been able to deceive him without primero by inviting him to play for a greater deposit. Similarly, if he invites a bet on the basis of a point, he is compelled to show two different cards and one of the same suit as one of them, in order that nobody may suspect him of having fluxus or primero.

19. On the Diversity of Points or Numbers in Primero

THE HIGHEST simple point after the greatest of all, which is the supremus, is 54, the lowest is 20, and therefore the mean is 37. However, on account of the supremus, 38 is considered the mean, but it cannot be made with two cards; therefore 39 is taken to be the mean, and if you have the superior position on the right of the dealer, it will be called the superior mean.

But in primero, when it cannot be beaten by supremus, nor by anything else except chorus, the highest is 78. But the highest without restriction is 84 and the lowest is 40. Therefore the mean without restriction is 59, or rather 62 if you are at the right. For 78 also on the left can be beaten by a similar hand, but 79 can be beaten in no way except by chorus. For chorus wins over everything and supremus may beat primero; but for one or the other of them the liberty of increasing the bets is taken away. Again in fluxus the lowest number is 42 and the greatest 70, so that the mean is 61. Let us therefore reason correctly: since the mean number from the beginning is 37, the greatest is 39 and the least is 34. They are made up from the highest cards combined in three ways, and they can make up the supreme point with the expectation of one card. Therefore, since there are 102 points in the other eight cards, and, in the game of primero 37 is the mean point of two (high) cards, the mean point is 50 in three cards, and of the rest twice 13, so the mean point will be 63. Thus, the same thing happens in fluxus as in primero; moreover, many varieties occur, both of the above-mentioned sort, of which greater or smaller varieties may appear, and of the sort which I shall mention.[12]

[12] The bids in primero were divided into high and low, and Cardano tries to explain how the dividing points may have been selected in each case.

For the point bids everything above and including 39 should be considered a superior point. To arrive at this figure Cardano recalls that 20 and 54 were the two extremes for the points and their mean is 37. Here the supreme point with the value 55 is not considered to be a point, but if this is done the mean becomes 37½ and thus 38 should be the starting figure for the high points. However, as Cardano argues, 38 cannot occur on two cards, therefore 39 is preferred.

In the case of the primero Cardano has to perform a similar juggling to make his argument fit the rule. When the chorus or four of a kind is counted as primero, the maximum is 84 and the minimum 40, giving the mean 62; thus superior primero should start at 63. This appears to be the correct figure, at least for the

20. On Luck in Play

IN THESE MATTERS luck seems to play a very great role, so that some meet with unexpected success while others fail in what they might expect; so that the above reasoning about the mean does not apply. For this mean is composed of extremes, not as in lawsuits, and valuations, and the like. For it is agreed by all that one man may be more fortunate than another, or even than himself at another time of life, not only in games but also in business, and with one man more than another and on one day more than another.

If anyone should throw with an outcome tending more in one direction than it should and less in another, or else it is always just equal to what it should be, then, in the case of a fair game there will be a reason and a basis

---

person in the lead to the right of the dealer. If the chorus is not counted, he arrives at the mean 59 based on the top value 78. However, this maximal value of 78 is hard to reconcile with the fact that 3 sevens and a six give a prime value of 81, while 3 sevens and an ace give 79. The bid of 78 consists of 2 sevens and 2 sixes.

Cardano's mean rule is still harder to fit in the case of the flush. The extremes are 42 and 72 as stated previously and Cardano first gives the mean erroneously as 61 instead of 57. However, he notices immediately that this does not lead to the conditions he wishes and he resumes his reasoning on a different basis.

We recall that when play begins each player has two cards and there may be considerable passing and drawing before one of them obtains cards which he considers sufficiently promising for an opening bid. In case he goes for a flush two high cards in the same suit would be the most desirable hand for making a *vada* ("it goes," the start of play). This would be either seven, six or seven, ace or six, ace; each of them can produce the supreme point with a single additional card, as Cardano observes. The corresponding point values are 39, 37, and 34. He assumes that a player opens with the middle high pair, a seven and an ace with the point value 37. There remain eight cards in the same suit and their point values add up to 102. Thus the average value for each of the remaining cards is 12¾ which Cardano rounds off to 13. He computes correspondingly that on three cards the average is $37 + 13 = 50$ and for a flush $37 + 13 + 13 = 63$ which is the same figure as for a primero and evidently the middle value he wishes to establish.

for it, and it is not the play of chance; but if there are diverse results at every placing of the wagers, then some other factor is present to a greater or less extent; there is no rational knowledge of luck to be found in this, though it is necessarily luck.

However, astrologers make claims for themselves; yet I have never seen an astrologer who was lucky at gambling, nor were those lucky who took their advice. The reason is as follows: although, as in all matters of chance, it happens that they occasionally make the right forecast, nevertheless, if they have guessed right (for when they do not guess right, they must lose) then immediately afterward they go very badly wrong, since they become venturesome and lose more from one mistake than they win from forecasting correctly four times in a row. For the path into error is always steeper, and the loss is greater than the gain.

And I have seen others who make their decision with the help of geomancy; but this is an unstable vanity and dangerous unless very moderate use is made of its deceptive help. As for the fact that some of them do make forecasts, this is to be explained on the ground that others make still more frequent mistakes. For since there is necessarily some inequality in this respect, one man will be right more often and another less. These statements appear likely to our reason.

Yet I have decided to submit to the judgment of my readers what happened to me in the year 1526 in the company of Thomas Lezius, the patrician of Venice, leaving it to each reader to form his own opinion. I had just duly resigned from the office of rector of the scholars in the University of Padua on the third of August, and now I was journeying with Hieronymus Rivola, a scholar from Bergamo, on a certain night of the same month toward Venice. We were playing a game (called Bassette) and I won all the money he had. Then he asked me to play with him on credit, if I am not mistaken, up to two or three aurei, and I won again. Then, finally, he wanted to carry it on endlessly, but I refused. He promised to pay what he owed me within three days; but he did not come.

Then he chanced to meet me and said that he would come to pay the money on Saturday (which was the day of the Nativity of the Virgin) and promised to take me to a beautiful prostitute. At that time I was just completing my twenty-fifth year, but I was impotent. Nevertheless, I accepted the condition; there was not a word about the game. He came on the day agreed; and in that year the festival of the Blessed Virgin was on Saturday. He took me to the home of Thomas Lezius; there was no Thais there, but a bearded man with a young servant. No money was paid but we played with marked cards. I lost to him all the money which he owed me, and he reckoned it as part of his debts just as though he had given it to me. I lost about twenty-five aurei or even a few more which I had, and played on, giving my clothes and my rings as security.

I returned home in sadness (as was natural), especially since there was no hope of getting money from home because uprisings and plots were raging at Milan. And so (and now I tell the truth, there being no reason why I should lie) I contrived for myself a certain art; I do not now remember what it was, since thirty-eight years have passed, but I think it took its rise in geomancy, by which I kept in mind on up to twenty-four plays all the numbers whereby I should win and all those whereby I should lose; by chance the former were far more numerous than the latter, even in the proportion (if I am not mistaken) of seven to one; and I do not recall now in what order these were against me.

But when I saw that I could not safely hold more numbers in my memory, I admonished my young servant, whose name was Jacob, that when he saw I had won back my clothes and my money he was to call me. I threatened that if he did not do it I would beat him severely. He promised and we went. As the game went on I won and lost in all the plays just as I had foreseen and after the third play I realized that there was no trickery or deceit about it. They laid down money freely and I accepted the wagers, but he was delighted by the example of the previous day and also on account of the marked cards (as I have said).

Thus his thoughts were inflamed by his youthful ardor; but the result was otherwise, for, on those plays in which I saw (as it were, without any real foreknowledge) that I would win, I did not reject any amount of money and made large bets of my own, and in the other cases, where I knew he would win, I refused if he was the first to wager, and wagered very meagerly myself: thus the result was that within twenty plays I regained my clothes, my rings, and money and also what he had added besides. As for the clothes, the rings, and a collar for the boy, I sent them home piecemeal. Out of the total number there remained four deals; I played and won, and also came out victor in a few deals which were not contained in the number.

He was already perturbed and full of admiration, since he saw that in all the plays in which we played for high stakes I came out the victor, and in those in which he won I myself wagered little and when he wished to wager a great deal I refused. So (he said) I believe some demon is advising you, or that you know by some enchantment what is going to happen. What happened after that I remember that I have narrated elsewhere.[13]

But now I return to the question at issue; if anyone should say that my Genius was advising me, although apparently he had never yet revealed himself, I will not dispute it; yet, there must have been some art by which the Genius himself had this foreknowledge. On this point (as I have said) I leave the decision to others.

[13] *De Vita Propria,* Chapter 20. See p. 129.

Now I think it worthy of consideration that this fortune of mine seems to have been something greater than mere chance, since we see in it a beginning, an increase, and a certain continuance so that certain remarkable things happen, as for instance that two aces occurred twice when defeat could not otherwise be brought about, and other things of this sort. We would also see a decline and then very often a change, and then great calamity or great good fortune, and other things in the same way. In view of all this I should think we ought to decide that there is something in this, although we do not know the law which connects the parts. It is as though you were fated in advance to be enriched or despoiled; especially seeing that from this there can follow something more important, as it happened to the man who, on leaving a game after losing all his money, injured the image of the Blessed Virgin with his fist. He was arrested and condemned to be hanged.

But whether the cause of that luck, be it in the conjunction of the stars or in the construction of a certain order of the universe, can affect the cards, which are considered bad or good only according to the conventions of men (since they signify nothing of themselves), is so worthy of doubt that it is easier to find a cause of this fact without that purpose than with it; without it the matter can well be reduced to chance, as in the constitution of the clouds, the scattering of beans, and the like.

21. On Timidity in the Throw

For this reason it is natural to wonder why those who throw the dice timidly are defeated. Does the mind itself have a presentment of evil? But we must free men from error; for although this might be thought true, still we have a more manifest reason. For when anyone begins to succumb to adverse fortune, he is very often accustomed to throw the dice timidly; but if the adverse fortune persists, it will necessarily fall unfavorably. Then, since he threw it timidly, people think that it fell unfavorably for that very reason; but this is not so. It is because fortune is adverse that the die falls unfavorably, and because the die falls unfavorably he loses, and because he loses he throws the die timidly. So, since the timid throwing of the die is fourth in order while the unfavorable falling is second, the fourth cannot be the cause of the second, neither the proper cause nor a concomitant, but rather the other way around. Therefore, the timid throw, provided that the die is honest and he does not seize it in a way suggested by his opponent, cannot be the cause of the unlucky number: it can happen for other reasons.

22. On the Twofold Division of Games

SOME GAMES use dice, that is, the play is open, and others cards, that is, the play is concealed. Each kind is again subdivided, since some games consist solely of chance, especially dice, and also primero and fluxus in cards. But some join to chance the art of play, as *fritillus* in dice and in cards *taro, ulcus, triumphus* and the like. Therefore it is established that games consist either of luck alone, or of luck and art, and since each kind can be open or concealed, it is clear that there are four fundamental kinds of games among those which consist in luck, and not in bodily strength or agility.

23. On Card Games in Which There Is Occasion for Trained Skill

SINCE here we exercise judgment in an unknown matter, it follows that the memory of those cards which we have deposited or covered or left should be of some importance, and in certain games it is of the greatest importance, as in *trappola,* the Venetian game. In this game the threes, fours, fives, and sixes are removed. In the four suits there are sixteen of these, so that thirty-six cards are left. They are dealt out, five at a time and then four; in the case of two players eighteen cards are dealt and the same number left in a pile; if the first player is satisfied with his cards, he retains them, and if the second player is dissatisfied with his, he exchanges them and receives the nine top cards on the pile; and if these please him, then he himself keeps them, but if not, he exchanges them again with the second pile.

So you see how much depends on memory, judgment, skill in avoiding deception with due regard for safety. Many players, then, although they remember well, do not avoid the stratagems of their adversary carefully enough, or do not play with foresight, or too timidly, or as though they were angry.

Therefore when I had settled in the town of Sacco I was delighted by this game in a wonderful way; from it I saw the beginning of all good fortune. For by careful attention I brought it about that I was always mindful of all the cards which I had discarded. But art is of very great importance in the play. For the player who gets the last card has six points; if it is a two, it is worth 25, the six points being due to its being the last card. The ten, since it is the smallest, unless it is alone, cannot fail to be beaten: but in last position it is doubled, and so is worth 20, and when 6 is added to this, it is worth 26; if this happens twice, that is, if the two is in both the last and next to the last position, it is worth 52, namely, 26 each; but if there are three twos they are worth 78, namely, 3 times 26. Since the three last cards are all twos, it would mean 104 if the 52 were doubled. But this is not right; for then it would be necessary that the last should be worth 26, the last together with the next to the last worth 78, and the third last, together with the other two, worth 234, which no one admits. But they agree on a custom or rule of this sort that the two also, if it is the first card, or among the rest, should not be beaten, since the adversary would lack cards of that suit. It is worth 10, but among some it is worth 12. The jack is worth 3 points, the queen (or the knight) 4, the king 5, the one they call *luneta,* as being supreme in its suit (and it conquers the king and all other cards), is worth 6; three lunetas before the play are worth 12, three twos are worth 10, three kings, or knights (or queens), or jacks are worth 6, and it is not necessary to say, except in the case of lunetas, what suit they are; but all of these, together with the two, are called by the name of face cards. But it is necessary for three to be alike and of one suit, as three twos, or three kings. It is not necessary that we should name the lunetas or face cards at the beginning of the game, but only before we show any of those three, or before we play, or in playing, provided we have not collected any of those; if any player gets all the cards, this is called *cucus*[14] and the whole score is doubled.

When I had reduced the memory of these cards to the knowledge of one word, I learned to include in this fashion in a single word many other things as well; and thence by practicing this invention a whole text and all that was contained in it. And after that passages were found and derived from authors, which led to extemporaneous declaiming.

But I return to the play of cards; seeing that this kind of game was most artificial, since it would depend on a fixed procedure and forced arrangements, I omitted all exercise of that kind of divination for many reasons. First of all, I betook myself to Padua and thence to Sacco and so I had no further opportunity for the game; for that type of chance does not have any place where skill is mixed into the game. Secondly, I was afraid that it might ruin me through being overconfident. Moreover, I said that, if

[14] The word means jackdaw.

it is deceptive because of the demon, it is thereby contrary to law, but if it depends on chance, then it is foolish to trust it. Also I shrank from a game which was condemned by the law. Moreover, I thought it foolish to wish to contend so absurdly when I could play under more profitable or safer conditions.

24. On the Difference Between Play with Cards and Play with Dice

CARD GAMES differ from dice games even when these require skill, because play with dice depends more on judgment of future events; mostly, to be sure, on the success of one's opponent but also on one's own success, while play with cards requires only judgment of one's present holdings and of one's opponent's. To conjecture about the present is more the part of a prudent man skilled in human wisdom; but to conjecture about the future, although it is another kind of guessing, not as to what will be, but what we may rightly count on, is nevertheless the part rather of a divine man, or of an insane one, for the melancholy are given to prophesy. For in play with dice you have no certain sign, but everything depends entirely on pure chance, if the die is honest. Whatever there may be in it beyond unfounded conjecture and the arguments given above should be put down to blind chance.

But in cards, apart from the recognition of cards from the back there are a thousand other natural and worthy ways of recognizing them which are at the disposal of a prudent man. In this connection the game of chess surpasses all others in subtlety. It is subjected little or not at all to the arbitrariness of chance. Similarly, exercise with weapons surpasses everything else in usefulness, play with balls surpasses in healthfulness, trappola in charm, primero in beauty of invention and variety, sanctius by the greatness of the stakes, fritillus in attentive competition with little fatigue, tarochi in the passing of time, cricones in dignity, and triumphus in prudence and imitation of human life. So it is more fitting for the wise man to play at cards than at dice and at triumphus rather than at other games; so it is agreed (but it is not in use) that this is a sort of midway game played with open cards, very close to the game of chess. It has an end when nothing further can be done and every game makes its own end. It is played with nine cards (for this is a satisfactory number) and is the mean between the great and the small; when the cards are placed on the table one begins to play, as one is accustomed to do with hidden cards. Since this is a most ingenious game, I am very much surprised that it has been neglected by so many nations.

25. On Card Games

THUS card games do not consist in expectation of future events except when cards are being exchanged. There are several kinds but it is not possible to enumerate them. For what Horace said about words can suitably be said about games: it will be sufficient to distinguish them by their kind and type, both simple and composite. First, therefore, are the kinds of games which depend solely on the arbitrariness of chance, and, secondly, those requiring attention and skill.

Dependent on chance only are *primero* and the *fluxus* which is played with three cards; the French type is the most beautiful; for an ace with a face card, or with a deuce, makes 21, which is the highest point among the other nations generally. But among the French, if another one is present, they make 21½. But three points surpass even fluxus and there is a *supremum* which can be considered either as a fluxus or as a point. Also, 20, together with a one or another card, makes 20½, and so they have 20, 20½,

21, 21½, and 22, which (as I have said) is superior to fluxus. Then comes *fluxada;* and *silerium,* which, in my opinion, is the same as 40 and 31. *Bassette* is the game of desperate men; then there is the game of *cricones,* which belongs to chance, and to skill belong *triumphi, triumfeti,* and variations of these, a variation of *tarochi, one hundred, trappola, romfa, scaltara,* and many others.

There is another division according to their peculiar differences, since some games involve judgment of the cards, whereas others do not but involve the drawing of cards. Some games by the number of cards, some by the estimation, some by the consequences, some by a fixed reckoning of the place or position, some by some other property, make up the whole number of types by which games may be classified as being superior or inferior.

26. Do Those Who Teach Also Play Well?

Perhaps someone will quite rightly ask whether the same people who know these rules also play well or not. For it seems to be a different thing to know and to execute, and many who play very well are very unlucky. The same question arises in other discussions. Is a learned physician also a skilled one? In those matters which give time for reflection, the same man is both learned and successful, as in mathematics, jurisprudence, and also medicine, for very rarely does the sick man admit no delay.

But in those matters in which no time is given and guile prevails, it is one thing to know and another to exercise one's knowledge successfully, as in gambling, war, dueling, and commerce. For although acumen depends on both knowledge and practice, still practice and experience can do more than knowledge. Also a certain physical acquaintance is of greater value in those matters where there is need of special knowledge, as in the appraisal of gems, paintings, and the recognition of counterfeit or genuine money.

So there are three elements in the case, not all of equal importance, namely, physical nature, acumen, and quickness. So it was right for Hannibal to make fun of the philosopher who had never seen a battle line and was discoursing on war. Thus it is with all games which depend on the arbitrariness of fortune, either entirely or together with skill, when they are played rapidly and time is not given for careful thought. Since physical games, depending on agility of hand or sharpness of eye, are subject to training, it is not surprising that to know is one thing and to exercise one's knowledge, and exercise it rightly, is another. In certain matters, as in military affairs, knowledge joined to practice is of great value, but not practice joined to knowledge; for what is the principal thing in each matter ought to have precedence and be the greater.

27. Is There Some Element Apart from Skill Which Plays a Role in the Exercise of Skill?

SINCE it is necessary, in addition to practice, which gives us experience, to have agility, quickness, keen senses, knowledge, and method, it remains to ask whether there is anything beyond all these things which contributes to victory in games. And I mean even where you have plenty of time for reflection; for that is the most important element, together with the judgment which arises from it.

Just remember the ridiculous story that was told about the knot which loosened for the man who had been hanged; thus some people have one thing and other people other things to report. There are stones which, as they claim, increase the skill of those who wear them and I know that the pearl is among them, and similarly other stones which increase boldness, as those which are called nicolos.[15]

[15] The nicolo was the popular name for the onyx. It was supposed to promote audacity and steadfastness.

However, there is no question here of these or of similar things, but (as we have said) we must discuss the question of luck. So, just as there is change of persons, ages, years, months, days, and hours, so change varies fortune; thus, in everything that changes, there is necessarily something, since it has been agreed that it changed. As for instance: if I were to be defeated tomorrow and win the day after, there would necessarily be something of such a sort as tomorrow and the day after tomorrow; perhaps someone will say that there is nothing except time, which changes or can change fortune, nor is this reasoning absurd, since the variety of time depends on fate, and other things not so.

If, then, it is to be or not to be, how can it be changed by amulets? This same argument demonstrates that neither a doctor nor a barber nor a war lord ought to heal better, or cut hair, or manage warfare better if they were without these things. Even if this should be true, since it is so absurd and contrary to human opinion and reasoning, I do not see how it could be admitted.

Let us therefore examine what this luck is and on what principle it depends; certainly it seems to me to be a disposition of affairs in accordance with or adverse to the will or plan of a man; so that no matter how you act, the matter turns out well or badly, or agrees with human plans or does not agree. Good fortune is twofold, like force and guile in human affairs, and it may suit our plan or deceive us. For if I stay at home or do not stay, it can turn out very badly either way; but whatever happens, we are subject to the authority of the Prince. So it is also in games. Therefore, there are two kinds of happenings and non-happenings, one of them absolute and the other relative to plan or judgment.

These matters are treated in the books about fate, but as far as the present question is concerned, it is sufficient to say here that fortune is changed by some principle, as a plan is changed, sometimes openly, as when I should go to war and experience a different fortune than if I should go on a journey or remain at home, but sometimes secretly as in gambling, as when I should shake more or less, and a different point should come forth with each different impetus.

Therefore, fortune works secretly in a twofold way, either by changing the plan from which action results or else by means of an event which is fortuitous in comparison with the existing circumstances. For example, I have an enemy, and his bad luck is thus part of my plan; but if his power should be increased by the marriage of his daughter, this pertains to luck and has nothing to do with my plan. Moreover, although the principle of the first of these two, namely, luck, is not clear, nevertheless it is beyond doubt.

We must therefore think that there is some method in each, and that it is possible to be blessed or to be unfortunate, in just the same manner as those who play while drunk, or angry, or in fear, or suspicion, things which are familiar to everybody.

But of the other method there is also some secret principle. To these matters belong amulets, witchcraft, and the like, and just as in each case (as they say) the sword fits its own sheath and the foot its own shoe, so the hour, the day, the year, and the place must fit; so also in this question, what will make one man happy will make another wretched. But most important seems to be judgment and foresight because it provides far-reaching counsel. For the other things admit ordinary treatment, namely, things which are evident and which extend to one throw or even to two.

28. On Far-reaching Plans, Judgment, and Procedure [in Backgammon]

OF THE GREATEST IMPORTANCE in gambling is foresight and judgment pertaining to many throws, as on the board matters are so arranged that there is a twofold way to our goal, the one that we advance more rapidly, the other that we retard our adversary; we advance more rapidly by occupying better positions, and more quickly, if on the contrary, we retard our adversary either in order that he may have worse positions and fewer or that he may fall behind in entering the last row.

Since, therefore, the ways are as stated, we advance as far in each of them as we can. But we must take care that we apply ourselves to the advance to a greater extent, but not entirely, since this can scarcely be done, seeing that, in order to proceed more quickly, you must take care to be safe from the incursions of your adversary and to impede him. Again two aims arise, whether you ought to proceed deliberately or, on the other hand, whether you ought to lie in ambush. Therefore, you have already four goals: to proceed easily into the best positions; not to be open to hindrance; to hinder him; and to lie in safe ambush if the occasion should arise to hinder him. But there are two ways to hinder him: either to block him off from his position or from the passage to it; or else to cast out his counters, so that they are forced to return to their original positions.

For you know that there are four tables on the board, each of which contains six points. But we could also foresee hindrance beforehand, so that there are six aims. The obstacle also should be either in several or in special places. The special places are directly opposite and where he is forced to transpose to his disadvantage. But to foresee these things far in advance calls for a certain skill which no art can teach in general. Or rather one can certainly teach it, but nobody can be of such judgment as to acquire it.

Therefore, I shall first teach it by one example, in order that the approach to all these matters may be easier. Suppose that you despair of victory because you are delayed, let us say, by a fourth part of the throws; for it is always necessary to refer the matter to what is left, and although the proportion may be the same, still, the closer it is to the end of the game, the more difference it makes. Therefore, you must consider whether your disadvantage is small and can be repaired by a change of luck, for then the game

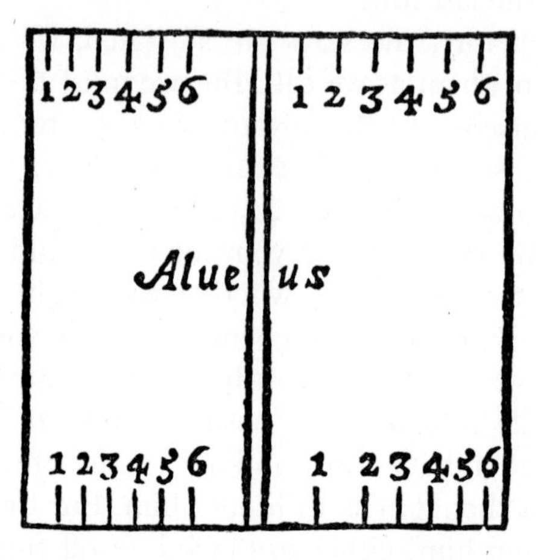

29. A backgammon board. From *De Ludo Aleae.*

is not to be conceded. Again, if you are closer to the end, although you can and ought to concede defeat, still you will not do so. Again, if you are farther away from the end but the opponent's men have already gone far in advance in comparison with your own, you ought not to contemplate such a great step. Therefore, when your hopes are far inferior to his and the game has not proceeded very far, and your men have not progressed to points from which they cannot by any means be extracted since they are not ahead of his, then it is necessary to think about returning them and blocking some point. When you have finished deliberating, it is desirable to find a means to concentrate entirely on this business and try to bring back the men which have advanced. Moreover, this should sometimes be done aggressively, which is both deceptive and dangerous, and sometimes slyly (though of course it can be perceived), a procedure which, as it is a matter of greater art, is also safer and more certain.

Having entered in this way upon general considerations, it is necessary to persevere. For this reason one must keep one's eyes open in this sort of business and especially consider whether one ought to act or not, and, if so, then whether openly or not. This judgment and counsel, this providence, both in details and in general, is deeper than human nature. It is like the prospect of the sky and of infinity. In general, however, higher points are usually blocked with greater advantage, for fear that the adversary may proceed, but the medium ones, like those which they call homes, are dissolved.

29. On the Character of Players

EVEN evil has its own laws, as in the case of robbers and pirates. There are some who with many words drive both themselves and others from their proper senses. I omit speaking of those who, as though they were insane, hurl invectives against the gods. Certain people are so contentious that they provoke others to such anger that they forget everything. Finally there are those who crack jokes to their adversaries; others are silent, which would be best if they did not demand the same from their adversaries.

There is a golden mean in everything; let a man play such that first of all he does not forget the opening moves and those plays which contribute toward victory, that he is not angry, that he does not provoke anger, that he is not afraid, that he does not talk nonsense, that he does not vex a partner, especially when one is losing. Let him remember himself, his adversary, the bystanders, the place. If the adversary is not of this type, it is better not to play. For as a little bile in a great deal of honey and a little bit of rottenness in a large mixture of pleasant things can do far more to produce vomiting than all the rest can do to produce delight, so a blameworthy adversary can, like a brandished sling, drive far away all the pleasure of the game and all the peculiar delights derived from it. That taciturnity which verges on utter silence is too hard and severe, since it is a greater pleasure to talk without playing than to play without talking.

30. On Games of Chance Among the Ancients

THE ANCIENTS had a game of chance which they called *tesserae*, although *alea* has usurped the common name of all games which depend on chance. The inventor (as they say) was Palamedes while the Trojan war was in progress. For they sat, according to the testimony of all, around that city for ten years, so that it was devised in order to relieve the tedium. Those objects are properly called tesserae which others call cubes, with six faces and the same number of points. It was forbidden in the Roman period except during the Saturnalia; whence Martial (Lib. 14.1) "and the slave shakes the dice box without fear of the aedile, since he sees so close at hand the freezing of the ponds." Nevertheless the cube seems to differ in some way from the tessera according to the statement of Vitruvius. The cube is an object of six sides with equal width of square plane faces. On whatever side it falls when it is thrown, and in good condition, it has a solid resting place; and the same is true of the tesserae which those players throw who play on a board; and they are called falls or throws among the Greeks. Our authority for this statement is Eustathius,[16] according to Caelius Calcagninus,[17] from whom we take this chapter and the following one.

[16] Eustathius, archbishop of Thessalonica (d. A.D. 1193), author

It is agreed that they have six planes, of which number the tessera also consists. The same Eustathius has told us that on each tessera the individual points on the opposite faces should add up to the same number, namely, seven, as six is opposed to one, and five to two, and four to three. This is done with the idea of making it easier to detect falsification, if anyone should make a false die, by duplicating the one and leaving out some other number. This is an especially disgraceful act, particularly if during the play the dice are thrown trickily by sleight of hand while the adversary's attention is distracted.

So it was our duty to add this chapter of review, not so much for the sake of the ancient customs as for giving information by means of which, when understood, something more useful could be derived. For as this was designed to remove the greatest fraud, it offers an occasion for a lesser one. For those who throw the points they want, by agility of hand, do so in three ways. First, in such a way that one die rides over the other, or so that one die rides over the two others if there are three of them: that is the best method and is called "to ride over" in colloquial speech, generally, "to change the die." A second method is more deceptive, and consists in letting the die cling to one of the sides or to two sides (of the board) and it is called in colloquial speech "spuntonum."[18] The third is not very safe, but is on the other hand very deceptive, when the die is thrown straight with such an impetus and such a number of points exposed above that it is probable that the point which we wish will come uppermost.

In all these matters it is of the utmost help that the cheat

---

of a famous commentary on Homer, where some of the ancient Greek games are discussed.

[17] Celio Calcagnini, *De Talorum ac Tesserarum. . . .* See Bibliography, Chapter 4.

[18] The word means halberd or spear.

should know how to throw the point in a certain position. Thus, it is not only of assistance to know that the six is opposite to the one and that the other points are in circuit, but also it is necessary to know exactly where, for instance, when the two and five are on the heads, the six and the one are on the sides (in figure, Chap. 9). So, against all these tricks they have devised the orc from the similitude of the fish. For it seems to devour the tesserae as the orc devours other smaller fish. Persius (*Saty.* 3): "not to be deceived by the neck of the narrow orc." Pomponius the poet of Bologna: "while contemplating the orc I have lost the little dice."

But the children inserted nuts into the orc so that the gambling object which he names is not the same as this one, although similar to it. Horace calls this *pyx* a *pyrgus*, thereby using a Greek word when he says (*Saty.* 9, *Sermon.* 2), "put the tali in the pyrgus." For they put in it not only tali but also tesserae; it is in constant use at Bologna but not at Milan. Martial calls it a *turricula*, whence in the *Apophoreta* on the turricula: "the wicked hand seeks to gather up and cast the tali; if it casts through me, it always produces what it wishes." This game of tesserae is modified so as to be played with the fritillus (for that is not the pyrgus but a gaming board; you may take it so, I do not contend about words); then you would say that with the board (if that is acceptable) the game is very similar to human life and, as it were, a modified example of what is stated in the *Adelphi* of Terence (Act 4, Scene 7): "The life of man is like when you play with the tesserae: if the best throw does not turn up, then whatever does turn up by chance, you must use to the best advantage." Moreover they played with two and with three tesserae; with two, for example, in the poem of Martial in the *Apophoreta* (14, 17): "Here for me the tessera is counted twice with a six." On the other hand, three are mentioned in the Greek proverb "either three sixes or else three ones."[19]

In our time also, games with the gaming board have become better known with three dice, *e.g. sperainum, speraia,* and *speraionum,* from which they also call the board itself sperainum; but in the colloquial language they call it *sbaraia* and *sbaraionum,* and similarly the little board *sbarainum.* Calcagninus thinks that sperainum is derived from "spargere" (to scatter), and *sbarainum* is that which would scatter. However that may be, all these games would be played with three tesserae; but we use two tesserae in a different way in sbarainum, since we always suppose the third die to be a six.

But sbaraia with three tesserae we call sbaraionum, as well as that game itself with three tesserae, but in it anyone may double the throws. This is the game of Princes and does not require thought; sbaraia is ingenious; sbarainum occupies an intermediate place; it is more in use because sbaraia is longer but sbaraionum depends mostly on luck. There are three other rather celebrated games with two tesserae, namely, *tocadiglium,* of which there are two kinds, the smaller, which depends on luck, and the greater, which requires far-seeing judgment; and there is also *canis Martius,* and tables, which are games requiring a moderate degree of skill; but canis Martius requires an outstanding intelligence.

In tables five men are placed in the last point from your right, and two in the first from your left; three in the second from your right and five in the sixth from your left, and your adversary places the same number in the corresponding places directly opposite to these. The most important consideration is to hinder the passage of your adversary's men and to strike them off. There is also another game which they call *Minoretum,* and there are two varieties of this, as of tocadiglium, namely, the greater and the

[19] Meaning: "highest luck or deepest despair."

smaller; in the latter it is not possible to reenter with a man which has been struck off, and the game is lost just as in tocadiglia when the pieces have been taken. But in greater tocadiglia, when this happens it is nevertheless up to the player's judgment whether he wishes to continue.

While the game of tesserae did not exceed the number of three, the game of tali had four, as will be seen below. So Martial says in the *Apophoreta*: "I, the tessera, would not wish to be equal in number to the tali, provided only the value of the throw should often be greater for me than for the tali." Ovid, moreover, tells us that the tesserae consisted of ivory, although in our times they are made of any kind of bone: "whether he shall play and throw the ivory numbers with his hand." In our times I have seen them made of rock crystal with gold points; tesserae are called by our contemporaries *Dati* because, in ancient times, they were accustomed to say that they played *datatim* (giving them to each other in turn), whence Plautus in the *Curculio*, "those slaves of the fine gentlemen who play datatim in the street"; and Pomponius, "when I played datatim with you in bed"; and Quintilian seems also, as that same Calcagninus avers, to have said, "remembering with what die he had gone wrong he returned to the one with which he had played"; but when he speaks about a game of twelve *scrupi* he seems to have referred the word datus to a game, but not to a game with dice. The cube (as I have said), they called *Monas* and sometimes *asinus*. Moreover, Midas was fortunate in his throws, whence the proverb,[20] "Midas, who is the best adviser in tesserae."

But this was only in one kind of game, very frequent and much practiced, as three sixes in the throw amongst us (2. *de arte amand.*): for this is superior to all the other numbers because it consists of three similar faces, and the highest at that; but of the beautiful games which are in

[20] The Midas throw may possibly have been the same as the Venus.

use, there is only sperainum, or sbarainum with two dice, which is without the six.

31. On Play with Knucklebones

KNUCKLEBONES were also made of ivory, as Martial says in the *Apophoreta,* "nor do the six and the one shake my ivory." I wished to say this because, although the talus is part of the back part of the leg of an animal, and in particular of a horned animal, those which were in use were nevertheless not natural tali but were made out of ivory or other material to resemble them, and were made smaller in order that they also, in the manner of the tesserae, might be enclosed in the pyrgus and be thrown out, and might not, by being placed together, fall according to the thrower's wish; it is agreed that tali and the Greek word *astragali* mean the same thing; Lysander used to say that children ought to be deceived with astragali and men with oaths. The saying was worthy of a Lacedaemonian, that is, of the worst kind of man; for nothing was more vile than that country which even Aristotle shunned, though he endured the Athenians, in whom there were innumerable disadvantages.

The talus is found in the joint of horned animals where the tibia joins the foot. It has six surfaces like all other bodies which are not round, on account of their three dimensions, since in each dimension there are two boundaries. But two of them are so small that it seems to have only four; one of them is humped up since it is curved, and on the opposite side it is concave and on each side it has a square, as it were, except that it narrows a little; on these are the one and opposite it the six, and then the three and four; and these are the four numbers with which the game with tali is played.

They call the one *Chios* and the six *Cous,* and when the one is compared with the six, the former is considered unlucky and the latter lucky. But when they are compared with the Venus, they are both unlucky. Whence Suetonius says, in the epistle about Augustus, "for when the tali have been thrown, if a player has thrown the dog or the six on a talus, they put a denarius in the middle for each, and then all of them were taken by the player who had thrown a Venus." Therefore, it is clear that the dog is the one, both because it is opposed to the six and because of those words about each talus.

So let us now consider composite cases: first, there may be four alike, as four aces, then a total of 12 with three alike, as (1,1,1,3), (1,1,1,4), and (1,1,1,6); and also (6,6,6,1), (6,6,6,3), or (6,6,6,4). But there are 18 cases of two alike. Thus all the throws of the knucklebones are 35. Among all these the most fortunate is the Venus, which consists of the dice presenting the natural position of the numbers, namely, one, three, four, and six, which is unique in knucklebones. But if it be compared to the total, it can happen in 24 ways, so that the four cases of all alike cannot happen more frequently:

All different	1
Four alike	4
Three alike	12
Two alike	18
SUM	35

Therefore, this one throw alone, which we call Venus, will happen 6 times as often as a throw with all alike. The three alike have 48 throws, but from the 6 throws two-alike and two-alike, since they can vary in 6 ways, there are 36 throws. The rest vary in 12 ways; therefore, there will be 144 throws; altogether, then, 256, of which number the number of similar ones, that is, four equal, is the 1/64 part:

$$4 + 24 + 36 + 48 + 144 = 256$$

But for the Venus the 24 cases is about 1/11, that is, it will happen that the Venus is thrown more often. Next to the Venus the most favorable throw was the *Stesichorius*, giving a total of 8, consisting of two ones and two threes. But it occurred in 6 cases only, wherefore it was considered among the rarest throws.

There was also the *Euripidean* throw, with four fours—it is counted 40, falsely, as some would say, because it cannot reach that sum. But that the Venerean throw was actually such is very clear from Martial, "when the tali have fallen for you with no face the same, you will say that I have given you great gifts." This is in the game for money; but the tali were also used to prophesy fate and the Venus was considered favorable and the dogs especially unfavorable, whence Propertius, "When I too was seeking Venus with favorable tali, the damned dogs always leaped out." Thus also in choosing the king at banquets according to that passage of Horace, "nor will you appoint by lot the arbiters of the wine"; and also this passage, "whom Venus names as arbiter of drinking." There was also another way, among children, of playing with tali, with an arbitrary number of them, just as they do now with little balls of lead, not contending for money but for the tali themselves. There is a story of this sort about Cupid, who won all the tali of Ganymede; these stories are well known but show the usual Greek levity. There are also other names for the throws, such as *Voltorius* and *Basilicus*, as Plautus says in the *Curculio*:

> *He invokes Planesius,*
> *He throws four voltorii.*
> *I seize the tali;*
> *I invoke my kindly nurse Heres;*
> *I throw Basilicus.*

He describes everything very well with one exception, namely, the four voltorii, that is, the fours; for they are long and thin and black and interpricked with white; this was the best point; but the parasite threw basilicus, which is probably the same as Venus; but on that basis I think it was the four sixes, since they strove for the highest point, not for the Venuses and the dogs; or if you wish, like the basilicus and the Venus, the vultures were sixes.

You will say, were not three sixes superior to four vultures? I reply no, since they were not alike, as I have also said in the game of tesserae about the throws. It would be permitted to bring up more cases here than with tesserae, since the total is 256 and of three tesserae 216, although the variety is more in the tesserae, namely, 56, but in the tali (as has been said) it is only 35.[21]

32. Conclusion of the Work

But in general it is to be observed, both for dice and for knucklebones, that since both of these complete the circuit in as many throws as there are faces, the die in six and the astragal in four, so in any one throw of any number of either dice or astragals, even if there should be a hundred of them, each makes up all possibilities in the same way. And so, if the total number shown by them be divided by the number of planes or faces, we get the average number.

Thus, in the case of six dice, one of which has only an ace on one face, and another a deuce, and so on up to six, the total number is 21, which, divided by 6, the number of faces, gives 3½ for one throw. However, the rule is not general; but in the case of most throws, it will turn out less than 3 on account of the excess of the greater numbers, which have to be computed.

But in the case of astragals, in order to determine the average number, add the greatest to the least, that is 4 and 24; the result is 28; half of this, 14, is the average number. So, when there is more than one ace, that throw is called the dog, because whatever the other dice may be, the throw

[21] Cardano here has the misprint 36.

cannot exceed the average number; from such a power of impeding, therefore, all throws with more than one ace are called the dog.

The same reasoning applies to finding the average number also in the case of three dice; for since the greatest is 18 and the least 3, added together they make 21, half of which is 10½, which is the average number.

By these pleasures it is permitted to relax the mind with play, in turmoils of the mind, or when our labors are light, or in great tension, or as a method of passing the time. A reliable witness is Cicero, when he says (*De Oratore*, 2): "men who are accustomed to hard daily toil, when by reason of the weather they are kept from their work, betake themselves to playing with a ball, or with knucklebones or with dice, or they may also contrive for themselves some new game in their leisure."

Index of Persons

Adam and Eve, 60
Alexander, 41
Appollo, 94
Archinto, Filippo, 12
Aretino, Pietro, 118
Ariosto, 104
Aristotle, 47, 69, 88, 153, 164, 194, 203, 237
Arlotto, Piovano, 87
Astolfo, 96, 97
Augustus, 80, 123, 238

Bartolotti, E., 63
Bassano, Zuan Antonio da, 65, 66, 67, 68
Beddingfield, 15
Bellini, A., 52n
Berni, Francesco, 114-116, 118
Borrel, Jean, 59, 60
Bottino, Salvatore, ix
Branda, 54

Caesar, 41, 42, 80
Calcagnini, Celio, 111-112, 168, 169, 232, 233n, 235, 236
Camuzio, 53
Cantor, Moritz, 106, 144
Cardano, Aldo, 17, 19, 20, 21, 23
Cardano, Brandonia Seroni, 18, 19
Cardano, Chiara, 17, 19
Cardano, Chiara Michena, 4, 5, 7
Cardano, Fazio, 19, 20, 23
Cardano, Fazio (Bonifacius), 3, 4, 5, 7
Cardano, Gasparo, 23, 81
Cardano, Giambatista, 10, 17, 18, 19
Cardano, Lucia Bandarini, 10, 17
Cardano, Niccolò, 40
Cassanate, 14
Castiglione, 27
Charles V, King, 7, 119, 120, 132

Christ, 14, 22, 30
Cicero, 123, 188, 241
Coi, Zuanne de Tonini da, 63, 65-69, 74, 79, 83, 87, 88, 97, 105
Copernicus, 48
Coué, 47
Croce, Annibale della, 11
Cupid, 239

Dalmagus or Damautus, 133
Dante, 115
d'Avalos, Alfonso, Marchese, 68, 71, 73, 74, 75, 77, 78, 81, 94

Eckman, J., 52n
Edward VI, King, 39
Erasmus, 55
Euclid, 66, 74, 101
Eustathius, 232, 233

Falstaff, 113
Fermat, viii, 177
Ferrari, Lodovico, 48, 74, 80, 81, 82-103, 105, 106, 107
Ferro, Scipione del, 62, 63, 65, 84, 85, 95, 98, 107
Fine, Oronce, 59
Fiore, Antonio Maria, 62, 63, 64, 65, 66, 67, 79, 83, 85, 98
Foix, Gaston de, 60
Fontana, 60
Francis I, King, 7, 119

Galen, 15, 47, 53
Galileo, 69, 160, 177
Ganymede, 239
Gargantua, 108
Geber, 74
Gonzaga, Cardinal, 81
Gonzaga, Ferrante di, 81, 99

Hamilton, James, 13
Hamilton, John, 13-14, 46
Hamlet, 42
Hannibal, 41, 136, 226

Hendrickson, G. L., ix
Henry VIII, King, 86
Heres, 239
Herod, 103
Hippocrates, 15, 47, 53
Homer, 233n
Homeromastix, 87
Horace, 224, 239
Huygens, Christian, 160, 177

Jacob, 217

Leibniz, 52
Lezius, Thomas, 122, 129-130, 136, 138, 211, 216, 217
Luca, Fra, 61, 62, 65, 85
Lucian, 87
Luther, Martin, 31
Lysander, 237

Mafio, 79
Martial, 232, 234, 236, 237, 239
Mary, Queen of Scots, 13
Maximilian, Emperor, 54
Mazarin, 114
Mendozza, Diego di, 88
Méré, Chevalier de, viii, 153, 154, 176
Midas, 236
Montmort, Rémond de, 143
Morley, H., 58n, 127-128

Nave, Annibale della, 62, 83, 84
Nemorarius, Giordano, 88
Nero, 14, 22
Nostradamus, vii, 40

Ovid, 236
Oxford, Earl of, 42

Pacioli, Luca, 61, 62, 65, 85
Palamedes, 232
Paracelsus, vii, 40
Pascal, viii, 153, 177
Peckham, John, 4
Persius, 234
Petrarch, 110
Petreius, Henrik, 22, 29
Petreius, Johannes, 11, 48
Pharaoh, 134
Piatti, Tommasso, 4, 10
Pietropaulo, 114
Pilate, 103
Pius V, Pope, 21
Planesius, 239
Plautus, 236, 239
Pompeius, Sextus, 123
Pomponius, 234, 236
Propertius, 239
Ptolemy, 74, 100, 102

Quintilian, 236

Rabelais, 108, 109
Richelieu, 114
Rivola, Hieronymus, 216

Saint-Gelais, Mellin de, 119
Scaliger, Julius Caesar, 54-58
Scotto, Ottaviano, 12, 73, 89
Seneca, 104, 186
Sforza, Francesco, 125, 133
Shakespeare, William, 42, 113, 117, 132
Silvestri, Rodolfo, 22, 23, 24, 81
Simon Magus, 134
Sorna (Soma), Francesco, 133-134, 212
Stesichorus, 170
Suetonius, 238
Suffolk, Duke of, 113
Sulla, 80

Tartaglia, Niccolò, 48, 59-61, 63-107, 177
Terence, 234
Thais, 217
Todhunter, Isaac, 144, 160

Vesalius, vii, 13
Vimercati, Antonio, 109
Vinci, Leonardo da, 3, 44, 61
Vitruvius, 100, 103, 232

Wentworth, Richard, 100, 104

Zoccolanti, Frati, 99, 102

Index of Subjects

Academicians, 41
Adelphi, 234
alchemy, 37, 122
algebra, 47, 61-62, 66, 177
allergy, 46
alveolus, 112
amulets, 21, 33, 123, 140, 142, 227, 228
Apophoreta, 234, 236, 237
arithmetic, 11, 48, 88, 100
arithmetic series, 163, 164
Ars Magna, 48, 79, 83, 84, 85, 86, 93, 107
arsenic, 19
artillery, 69, 72
asthma, 46
astragals, 143, 166, 168-171, 176, 237
astrologers, 39, 137, 216
astrology, 37, 40
astronomy, 14, 37-38
atheism, 28
Athenians, 237
Autobiography, 5, 9, 22, 23, 26, 27, 34, 37, 40, 43, 53, 58, 78, 81, 109, 120, 124, 137
average number, 240, 241

Babel, 60
Babylonians, 62
backgammon, 111, 112, 159, 176, 229-231
baldachin, 132
ballistics, 68
Basel, 29, 120
basilicus, 239, 240
bassette, 112, 114, 216, 225
Bergamo, 216
betting, 53, 117, 149
bidding, 116-117, 118, 173
blood-letting, 46
Bologna, 20, 21, 54, 80, 81, 84, 85, 89, 95, 96, 122, 126, 234; University of, 19, 48, 62, 81
bookkeeping, double entry, 61
Brescia, 60, 63, 85, 97, 100, 101, 102, 103, 104, 105

Canis Martius, 112, 235
Capitolo del Gioco della Primiera, 115
cardan, 120
cardinal(s), 22, 23, 127, 187
cards, 49, 112-113, 127, 132, 136-137, 140, 143, 172-175, 185, 206-214, 220-225; marked, 126, 129, 210, 217, 218
Catholic Church, 21, 31, 34
census, 64
challenge cartel, 86, 92, 95, 96, 98
chance, 136-137, 146, 154
cheating, 126, 129, 131-132, 134, 172, 173, 176, 210-212
chess, 14, 108, 109, 111, 112, 121, 122, 125, 126, 185, 195, 223, 224
chiromancy, 36, 141
chorus, 116, 207, 208, 212, 214
Christian(s), 30, 195
Church of the Augustins, 23
circuit, 148, 149, 156, 157, 163, 193, 195, passim
College of Medicine, 132
complex numbers, 82
consensus, 211
Considerazioni sopra il Giuoco dei Dadi, 160
Consolation, 15, 31, 42, 50
contest, challenge, 61, 63, 74, 80, 88
Cornelian Laws, 185
corrigiola, 71
cosa, 62
Cossick Art, 62
Counter-Reformation, 21
crap game, 111
cricones, 113, 225
critical number, 154

cube and cosa, 62, 64-66, 76, 84, 85, 94, 106, 107
cucus, 222
Curculio, 236

De Ludo Aleae, viii, 49, 115, 120, 122, 124, 126, 127, 129, 144, passim
De Malo Recentiorum Medicorum Medendi Usu Libellus, 12
De Perspectivis Communis, 4
De Propria Vita, see *Autobiography*
De Rerum Varietate, 22, 29
De Subtilitate, 22, 30, 43, 44, 55, 121, 134, 212
De Utilitate, 122
debate, public, see "disputes"
dice, 109, 111, 121-123, 126-127, 132, 140, 143, 144, 147-168, 171-172, 176, 177, 186, 190-193, 195-205, 219-220, 232; blind, 172, 176; change the, 132, 233; ride the, 132
disputes, public, viii, 7, 47, 53, 54-55, 61, 62, 96, 99-103, 105
divination, 35, 37, 40, 222
doctors, 187, 194
dog, 171, 240, 241
Dominican Order, 22, 29
draw, 172-175
Duke of Milan, 125, 127, 187
duodecim scripta, 111

Edinburgh, 14
education of children, 17
elements, 185
equality, 149, 150, 154, 155, 156, 159, 165, 193, 195, passim
equations, 100; fourth degree, 83; third degree, 69, 82
escutcheon, 26
Ethics, 194
eulogy, 55-58
Euripidean, 239
evolution, 44

falling bodies, 69
fare a salvare, 117, 120, 172-175
feathers, 46
Ferrara, 89
Florence, 89, 96, 160
flush (fluxus), 112, 116, 117, 174, 175, 207, 208, 209, 212, 213, 214, 224
fluxada, 225
formula, Cardano's, 167
French Geleus, 213
frequencies, 112, 160, 161
fritillus, 111, 112, 121, 122, 144, 151, 158-162, 185, 198-199, 220, 224

gamblers, 131, 135, 187
gambler's handbook, 126
gambling, viii, 8, 49, 120-140, 185, 186
games, 108, 120-121, 125, 136, 147, 172, 176, 185
Genius, protective, 33, 35, 138, 218
Geography, 100, 102
geomancy, 37, 136, 138-139, 216, 217
God, 30, 31
golden mean, 131, 231

hanging dice box, 191
hazard, 111
Heathen, 30
Henry VIII, 113
heresy, 21, 28, 34, 50
Holy Roman Empire, 119
Holy See, 118
horoscope(s), 3, 22, 31, 37, 38, 40, 130

illegitimate, 3
impotent, 6, 217
index of the Spanish Inquisition, 43

inquisition, 22, 28, 43
irreducible case, 82

Jew, 30
jurisprudence, 136

kermisses, 172
kibitzers, 134, 190, 211
knucklebones, 185

Lacedaemonian, 237
Latin, 28, 41, 55, 61, 92
lawyers, 187, 194
lectures, 10, 19
legerdemain, 132-134, 233
Length and Shortness of Life, 186
Libellus Qui Dicitur Computus Minor, 11
Lombardy, 71
London, 39
luck, 136, 138, 140, 142, 146, 147, 211, 215, 220
luneta, 222
lute, 186
Lyons, 24

magic, 26, 37, 40, 50
mathematical expectation, 149
mathematician(s), 47, 48, 59, 84, 87, 106, 107, 146, 202
mathematics, 3, 11, 14, 47, 48, 49, 60, 61, 62, 80, 84, 87, 136, 143, 177
mean, 171, 176, 213, 214; reasoning on the, 137, 145, 150, 151, 152, 153, 155, 158, 162, 165, 170, 171
medical doctor, 189; practice, 9, 12-15, 17, 23, 109; questions, books on, 14-15; sciences, 3, theories, 28, 44-46, 53
medicine, 47, 87, 136
Medicine, College of, 132; Doctor of, 8; professor of, 17, 19
melancholy, 122-123
Merry Wives of Windsor, The, 113
metoposcopy, 35
Milan, vii, 3, 4, passim
Minoretum, 235
miracle, 41
mirrors, 132, 211
Mohammedan, 30
noon, 191
music, 49, 88, 127
Mysteries of Eternity, 79
mysteriousness, 26

Naples, 133, 212
nard or nerd, 111
nicolos, 140
numerus, 116, 207
Nürnberg, 11, 48

oath of secrecy, 77, 83, 90, 95
occult, 3, 35, 37, 40, 50, 137
odds, 165, 175, 201, passim
one hundred, 113, 225
orc, 234
organum, 132, 211
originality, 49

Padua, 9, 89, 130, 222; University of, 7, 216
palmistry, 36
papyrus, 185
parchment, 185
Paris, 59
Pavia, 5, 17, 19, 53, 54, 89, 91; University of, 4, 7, 119
permutations, 157, 170
Philippic, 188
philosopher(s), 25, 146, 164, 189
philosophical, philosophy, 15, 31, 54
physician, court, 13, 120
Physicians, College of, 9, 10, 12-13, 23
physics, 14
Pisa, 69, 89, 96
plague, 5
poesia bernesca, 115
poker, 113, 116

police, 130
poorhouse, 10
pope(s), 21, 23, 118, 119, 120
post-mortem, 23
pot, 117, 119, 149, 173
Practica Arithmetica et Mensurandi Singularis, 11
Practica Arithmeticae Generalis, 78
premonitions, 33
prestidigitators, 132-133, 212
prime, 113
primero, 112-122, 172-175, 185, 206-212, 223, 224
Prince, authority of the, 147, 227
prism, 166, 169
probability, ordinary, 148; theory of, viii, 50, 137, 148, 177; additive properties, 162; law of large numbers, 143, 170-171; power law, 143, 164, 167, 176; repetition of an event, 145, 164, 167
problem of de Méré, 153-154, 176
psychiatrist, 46
publication, 63
pyrgus, 111, 234, 237

rack, 188
reals, 109
rector, rectorship, 7, 120, 132, 216
Reformation, 31
religion, 25
Renaissance, vii, viii, 30, 81, 108, 114, 115, 118, 147
reputation, 12, 13, 34, 109, 128, 135
rest, 117
Roman Empire, 41-42
Rome, vii, 1, 21, 23, 34, 89, 96, 116, 120
romfa, 113, 225

Sacco, 9, 10, 221, 222
Salerno, 89
San Marco, 23
sanctius, 113, 223
sanity, 34, 50
Saturnalia, 232
sbaraia, sbarainum or sbaraionum, 112, 235
scaltara, 113, 225
scepticism, 28, 137
Scotland, 13-14, 39
senator, 129-130
sense of humor, 115, 138
sentence, 22, 23
shower baths, 46
silerium, 225
sors, 158, 198-199
speraia, sperainum or speraionum, 112, 235
spuntonum, 233
stake(s), 109, 116, 117, 127-128, 149, 172-174, 187, 192, 212
Stesichorus, 170
Summa de Arithmetica, Geometria, Proportioni e Proportionalitá, 61, 65
supernatural, 33, 35, 138
superstitions, superstitious, 15, 34, 36, 39, 137
supreme point (supremus), 116, 119, 207, 214, 215, 224
swallow, 27
syphilis, 46

tables, 109, 111, 159, 192, 235
tali, 166, 168-171, 234, 237, 239
taro, 112, 220
tarochi, 112, 224, 225
tarok, 113
tesserae, 112, 232, 233, 234, 240
Thessalonica, 232n
tic-tac (tric-trac), 111
Titian Laws, 185
tocadiglium, 112, 235
trappola, 70, 71n, 112-113, 121-122, 137, 220, 223, 225
tricks, psychological, 134

triumph (trumps), 113, 121, 220, 224, 225
triumphetti, 113, 225
turricula, 234
typhus, 44

ulcus, 113, 220
universal joint, 120
urns, 167

vada, 116, 119
Venice, 7, 9, 12, 48, 61, 62, 65, 68, 78, 79, 89, 91, 95, 97, 100, 103, 105, 129, 131, 211, 216
Venus, 169, 170, 238, 239, 240
Verona, 89
Virgin, the, 14, 30, 129, 219
virginals, 186
voltorii, 239

wager(s), 146, 193, 200, 202, 213, 216; law of, 148
warts, 36
whip shot, 132
Wisdom, 15
witches, 37